RSACS

D1067812

D

JA

CHAMPION OF LIBERTY

HENRY KNOX

Born: July 25, 1750
Died: October 25, 1806

Henry Knox overcame boyhood poverty to become a prosperous bookseller at twenty, a fighting general at thirty, the
first U.S. Secretary of War and a founder of the state of
Maine. Knox's military knowledge had come from books, but
he was so skillful and dedicated that George Washington
chose him as commander of artillery in the ragged army that
rose to challenge the armed might of the British Empire. His
courage, energy, idealism and indomitable optimism enabled
him to perform near-miracles on the battlefield. After the
final triumph at Yorktown, he applied his skills to unite the
thirteen colonies into a strong nation, and to protect it from
rebellion at home, Indians on the frontier and foreign powers
abroad. This is the inspiring story of a man who embodied the
ideals of the nation he did so much to create and preserve.

Champion
of
Liberty

HENRY KNOX

by Justin F. Denzel

Julian Messner   **New York**

Published simultaneously in the United States and Canada by
Julian Messner, a division of Simon & Schuster, Inc.,
1 West 39 Street, New York, N.Y. 10018. All rights reserved.

To Jo and Ken

Printed in the United States of America
SBN 671-32069-6 Trade
671-32070-4 MCE
Library of Congress Catalog Card No. 69-13046

CHAMPION OF LIBERTY

HENRY KNOX

1

HENRY KNOX stood in the little kitchen of his home gazing out the window toward Boston Harbor. His mother, a thin, tired-looking woman, sat in a chair next to the rough, wooden table. Her eyes were red and wet from crying, and at her feet a three-year-old child played on the floor with a piece of string.

With a trembling hand the woman dabbed at her eyes. "He means well," she said. "He's going to try again in a new land. Maybe this time it will work out."

Henry nodded. "I know, Mother. As soon as he gets settled he's going to send for us." Henry knew this wasn't quite true, but he said it anyway. What he couldn't understand was why his father had left the country. For here, in this new land of America in 1759, there were unlimited opportunities. You had to work for them, but they were here, right here in Boston, not in some far-off island in the West Indies. "I'm sure it's going to be all right," he said, trying to reassure her.

"Only we haven't any money," his mother said. "He needed it all for the trip. We've only enough left for a few days."

Henry turned from the window. He was an unusually husky lad for his age. He had a round, lively face with warm, gray eyes full of buoyancy and good humor. Even now he seemed cheerful and unworried. "We'll manage," he said. "I can get a job down at the docks or the tannery."

The woman twisted her handkerchief nervously around thin, worn fingers. "But you're only nine years old. You should have a chance to finish school."

Henry walked over and picked the child up in his big hands, swinging him lightly over his head. The youngster giggled with delight. "There's you and little William to look after now," he said. "School will have to wait."

An hour later he was walking down the cobblestone street toward the docks. The towering masts of schooners and brigs loomed over Boston Harbor, and flocks of herring gulls wheeled and circled in the blue sky. As he walked along he thought of how suddenly life had changed. Yesterday he had been a lighthearted, carefree boy, playing leapfrog and flying kites with David McClure and the other youngsters of the neighborhood. Today his father had sailed off to the West Indies, leaving him penniless and the sole support of a small family.

It was a difficult situation, but then these were difficult times—times of change and uncertainty, when a boy came to manhood early and was expected to assume his share of burdens and responsibilities. Now, with his usual cheerful outlook, Henry was determined to make the best of it. He'd find a job and do what had to be done.

But down at the bustling docks his easy hopes were soon dashed. The yardmasters shook their heads, the deckhands smiled. It was the same story at the forge and the tannery. "Come back when you're fourteen," they told him.

It was dark when he got home, and he went directly to his little room without telling his mother. For a long while he lay awake, thinking. In some way he knew it wasn't fair to blame his father. Life had dealt harshly with William Knox. He had come to America in 1729 with a group of Scotch-Irish immigrants to find freedom and a new life. At first he prospered. Settling in Boston, he became a ship's master and the owner of wharf property on Sea Street. He married pretty Mary Campbell, and they moved into a large two-story house overlooking the harbor. Here ten sons were born. Only four of them reached maturity, and the two eldest of these, John and Benjamin, were later lost at sea. Henry, born in 1750, and his younger brother, William, born in 1756, were the only remaining sons.

Then in the mid-1750s, with the gradual decline of trade and the higher regulations on exports, the shipping business began to fall off. William Knox went deeper and deeper into debt in a vain attempt to save what remained of the business. But it was no use. Little by little his assets turned into liabilities, and he was forced to sell out. Now, in 1759, bitter and disappointed, he sailed away to the island of St. Eustatius in the West Indies to start a new life and perhaps a new fortune.

Henry thought of all this now as he lay in bed staring at the rafters. Yet he knew it was no use worrying about the past. He would have to think about the future now. He would have to think about tomorrow.

The next morning he was up early making the rounds of the merchants along King Street. They didn't pay as much as the docks or the tannery, but it would be a start. It would take care of the rent and put a little food on the table. He went from place to place, from wheelwright's to greengrocer's, from silversmith's to countinghouse, but without success.

Finally he reached Cornhill and the bookshop of Messrs. Wharton and Bowes. With some hesitation he went in and found himself surrounded by long rows of books, monographs, almanacs, maps and miscellanea. He made his way through the aisles, stopping here and there to examine the titles, browsing slowly from book to book. There were histories and encyclopedias, volumes on science, philosophy and religion, the very names of which generated a spark of curiosity in his eager young mind. For a while he went unnoticed; then from the rear of the store a tall, stern-looking gentleman approached. He planted himself directly behind Henry. "Is there something special you were looking for?" he asked.

Henry looked up, startled, suddenly brought back to his immediate problem. "I'd like to speak with the proprietor."

"I am Mr. Bowes, one of the owners. What is it you want?"

"I'm looking for work."

"And what can you do?"

"Anything that needs doing," said Henry. "I can run errands, take stock, wrap packages, sweep up."

Mr. Bowes pursed his lips and scratched the side of his cheek with a bony index finger. "Perhaps you can," he said. "But we need a full-time clerk, not a schoolboy."

Briefly Henry explained his circumstances while Bowes listened attentively. "So I've got to quit school and find a job," he concluded. "I'm strong and I can do the work of a man."

Mr. Bowes studied him for a moment or two. He must have liked what he saw. "All right," he said. "Tomorrow morning then. We don't pay much, but the work is steady and you'll have a chance to learn the business." As Henry started for the door, Mr. Bowes called after him: "I think you may even find it interesting."

He was right. The work was stimulating and rewarding, and Henry took to it instinctively, showing a natural flair for books and scholarship. He learned quickly, and his helpful manner and cheerful disposition soon made him a favorite with customers and employers alike.

Mr. Bowes particularly took a fatherly interest in the boy, guiding and advising him in matters of education and morals.

"Read," he once told Henry. "Read whenever you get the chance. Don't waste your time on idle chatter or petty gossip when you can listen to the greatest minds of the centuries speaking to you through books."

And so, as the years passed, Henry read. In between taking stock and waiting on customers he read Plutarch's *Lives* and Macaulay's *History of England*. He was especially interested in military history and engineering, and read the works of the Greek and Roman conquerors, the lives of famous generals and the military memoirs of the times. He studied the classics in translation and taught himself to read and speak French. His eager mind thirsted for knowledge, and he avidly delved into science, philosophy and the arts. Little by little, in spite of his lack of formal schooling, he managed to acquire a sound and liberal education among the stacks and volumes of the Wharton and Bowes bookshop. He even took books home with him, and in the evenings he and William sat around the kitchen table reading while their mother sewed or baked bread for the following day.

Yet, in spite of this scholarly tendency, Henry was no recluse. He found time to play, to go hunting and to enjoy himself in other outdoor activities. By the time he was sixteen he was a big, strapping fellow well over six feet in height, slightly on the portly side, with a deep, booming voice to match. He loved people, and he loved a good joke, laughing uproariously at the slightest bit of comedy or humor. And he was never so happy as when he was participating in some form of rough-and-tumble game or sport.

He regularly took part in the annual Guy Fawkes Day celebrations which pitted the tough North-Enders against the hard-bitten South-Enders in a wild free-for-all that usually lasted into the early hours of the morning. Amid ringing cheers and a flaming torchlight parade the rival teams pulled their heavy carts, bearing effigies of the Pope and the Devil, toward the center of town. Here they met in head-on collision, each team doing its utmost to demolish the other's effigy. On one memorable occasion the South-Ender's cart broke down on the way to battle. That was a catastrophe of the worst order, meaning almost certain victory for the opposition. Undaunted, Henry Knox removed his jacket and put his brawny shoulder under the axle, bearing the heavy wagon through the streets to the scene of action and helping to bring the riotous celebration to a successful conclusion.

Beneath this surface of frivolity and fun flowed a strong current of serious indignation as over the years Henry saw the people of Massachusetts turn from peace-loving, industrious citizens into embittered, angry men. The change took place slowly as the British Government stubbornly pressed the colonists for more and more revenue. Badly in need of money, the English King imposed tax after tax on the hapless Americans. There was a tax on sugar and molasses, on coffee and wine, on pig iron, hides and textiles. Duties and tariffs were collected on silks and linens, on glass, lead, paint, paper and tea, on everything that came into or went out of the country. Hardly an item existed that did not carry some form of tax or levy. Regulations restricting business were enacted, strangling the very flow of commerce. American ships carrying American goods had to put in at English ports before going on to Europe, thus doubling the price of exports and severely diminishing the market for American goods.

After years of slow, simmering resentment the colonists reached a point of open defiance. English goods were boycotted and secret anti-British organizations sprang up in towns and villages. Goon squads roamed the streets, ransacking and looting the homes of tax collectors and officials. In Boston, New York, Charlestown and Philadelphia, mobs marched in protest, threatening resistance and even violence. Sabotage, sedition and conspiracy brewed on every street corner, in every tavern and in the gray, shadowy mists along the waterfront. Pamphlets and leaflets advocating civil disobedience were distributed by the thousands throughout the towns and countryside. Everywhere the people were rising up against their oppressors.

Growing up in the midst of all this intrigue and political furor, Henry was quick to see the plight of the farmer, the merchant and the small-business man, and he felt the justice and righteousness of the colonial cause. In the busy book store of Wharton and Bowes, where Tory and rebel alike met and mingled, he frequently heard the argument hotly contested. A new sense of freedom and independence filled the air and Henry thrilled to the heady wine of its promise. He was an American not an Englishman, he was a freeman not a slave and he made no secret of his feelings.

Yet even during these years of political tension the British authorities sanctioned and even encouraged the formation of local militia units. These were small bands of citizens, trained and drilled in the use of muskets, bayonets and other weapons.

Caught up in the spirit of the times, Henry joined a local company of artillery known as the "Train." It was made up of men from the South End of Boston—tough, young mechanics, brawny blacksmiths, dockworkers and storekeepers. Periodically they met on the common, decked out in their splendid red and blue uniforms and manning their fieldpieces, their three-pounders and ammunition carriages. Under the watchful eyes of the British they learned to unlimber their cannons, swing into position, ram home the charge and fire. They learned to dig trenches and plan defensive positions. For a brief period in 1766 a company of Royal Artillery, on their way to Canada, stopped off in Boston. While waiting for orders they instructed the members of "The Train" in the latest tactics and maneuvers, thus unwittingly training these young patriots in the use of vital weapons that would soon be turned against them on the field of battle.

Playing a leading role in these martial activities, Henry Knox soon became known for his unusual qualities of leadership and authority. His friendly disposition and forthright character made him a trusted and respected citizen.

In the meantime the tension between the colonists and their English overseers continued to increase. Ugly incidents occurred almost weekly. There were beatings and sabotage, ships were hijacked and cargoes destroyed, warehouses burned and gutted.

To suppress these activities and protect the property and lives of citizens loyal to the Crown, the British sent troops into Boston. They were camped on the common and quartered in public buildings. Ostracized and rejected by the people, the soldiers soon became arrogant and bold. They walked the streets looking for trouble— insulting women, abusing merchants and in general making themselves obnoxious.

To the citizens, already angered to the point of rebellion, this was the final blow. A slow, smoldering fire burned just below the surface, and now the stage was set for violence. It happened on the cold, wintry night of March 5, 1770.

It was nine o'clock in the evening as Henry came down Cornhill. He had been visiting friends in Charlestown and was on his way home. A cold wind was coming in off the harbor, and patches of late snow still clung to the cobblestone streets. As he neared King Street he heard the bell ringing in the tower of the old brick meeting house. Instinctively he quickened his pace, thinking it must be a fire. Then, as he reached the customs house, he saw a wild, milling throng of some two hundred people. Many of them were fully dressed, but others were clad only in nightshirts and clogs. They were carrying clubs, fence pickets, fire tongs or any other weapon that came easy to hand. At the same time, Henry saw a barrage of snowballs and chunks of ice flying through the air accompanied by the angry shouts of "Kill the Lobsterbacks. Send them back to England, where they belong."

Quickly he managed to shoulder his way through the

mob. "It's Knox," one of them said. "It's Henry Knox." And they moved back to let him pass. His deep voice boomed over the turmoil. "What's going on?" he asked. "What's happened here?"

An angry, red-faced man stepped out of the crowd. He was brandishing a pitchfork. "It's the Lobsterbacks," he shouted. "Them Redcoats. They've beaten the barber's boy. Now they threaten to cut down the people. It's the Devil for them I say. Drive them out of town."

Henry held up his hands, pleading for order. Pushing his way to the center of the trouble, he came upon a small group of British soldiers lined up in the street, their muskets and bayonets facing the irate mob. Their faces were flushed with rage, their fingers itching on the triggers.

Without waiting to see more, Henry approached the nearest soldier, speaking to him in a firm, steady voice. "You are aware that if you fire that weapon without orders you may pay for it with your life?"

The soldier looked up, his eyes burning with hate. "Damn them, then," he said. "If they press me further I will fire. Now order them to stand back."

Henry turned, begging the crowd to move back, but the people were whipped into a frenzy and were in no mood to obey. They pushed against the points of the bayonets, taunting the soldiers, daring them to fire, striking at the leveled weapons with clubs and shovels. "Kill the Bloodybacks," they shouted. "Run them out of town."

A few moments later a red-coated officer of the guard came up. Henry recognized Captain Preston and ran up to him, grasping him by the front of the coat. "For God sakes," he said. "Get your men out of here. Take them back to the barracks. If anything happens you must bear the consequence."

Irritated and confused, Preston pulled himself away. "I know my duty," he growled. "I will not give the order to fire, but I intend to stand by my men." With that he placed himself squarely in front of the muskets and glared back at the unruly mob.

Once more Henry tried to calm the people, telling them to go home, that justice would be done. A few obeyed, but most of them only pressed closer, the ringleaders shouting defiance, daring the soldiers to fire. Then more snowballs and jagged pieces of ice were hurled through the air.

Suddenly a flying club struck one of the soldiers a glancing blow, knocking him to the ground. Slowly, in a daze, he pulled himself to his feet. At the same time, a voice in the crowd shouted, "FIRE!" Without thinking, the soldier pulled the trigger. His musket barked, shattering the darkness with orange-blue flame. The nearest man clutched at his chest and with a sickening gasp fell headlong into the snow. There was a moment of shocked silence, then more shots rang out.

Instantly the mob began to disperse, to flee for its life; but before it was over, five men lay dead and bleeding in the snow and seven more were seriously wounded.

That night Boston grumbled like an angry beast as armed militia units arrived from the surrounding areas, gathering on the street corners in small, surly bands. British troops were called out in strength, and all night long the sound of drums and marching feet echoed through the city.

By morning an ominous lull had settled over the common. An indignant assembly met with the British authorities in Faneuil Hall, demanding justice and quick retribution. The British troops were quickly moved to Castle Garden, five miles away, and the Governor promised a full and complete investigation with a trial to follow.

Within a few weeks the mood of the city returned to normal, and it looked as if the Boston Massacre would pass quietly into history and be forgotten. But Henry Knox and many of his compatriots knew that it was only the beginning.

2

FOR A FEW YEARS after the Boston Massacre, tension between the colonies and the mother country relaxed. Times were good. Trade began to pick up, and Henry decided to go into business for himself. During his long years with Wharton and Bowes he had worked hard. He had learned the business and prospered and at the same time managed to put aside a little money.

His father had never come back, having died on the island of St. Eustatius, in the West Indies, at the age of fifty. His mother died in 1771, and Henry decided he was now free to risk his small investment. Consequently, on July 29 of that same year, he experienced a feeling of pride and elation as he saw his little advertisement appear in the pages of Edes & Gill's *Gazette*.

This Day Is Opened
A New London Book Store by
HENRY KNOX
Opposite William's Court
Boston

The store carried a full line of dictionaries, almanacs and bibles, along with books on science, health, religion, history and travel. Fiction, too, was a popular item of the day, including such titles as *Tom Jones, Tristram Shandy, The Vicar of Wakefield, Pamela* and *Robinson Crusoe.*

With the help of William, who was now fifteen, Henry operated the little shop. William put up stock, swept out the store and ran errands while Henry waited on customers and kept the accounts.

In spite of his huge bulk and gruff voice, Henry was gracious and polite. He treated his customers with courtesy and respect, catering to their tastes with tact and understanding. He made no secret of his feelings in matters of politics. Yet the British officers and wealthy Tories flocked to his store, using it as a meeting place for local gossip and intellectual exchange. Rubbing shoulders with this well-educated gentry, Henry soon acquired their urbane and courtly manners. They, in turn, found him to be a generous host and a well-informed conversationalist.

With his keen interest in military subjects, Henry especially enjoyed his discussions with the friendly British officers, particularly members of the Royal Artillery. They frequently gathered in the back of his store—the young subalterns and captains, with their powdered, white wigs and their blue and red uniforms, poring over maps and manuals, arguing and debating the proper maneuvers, the latest tactics. One of them might have traced an imaginary line on the map with his forefinger. "In a situation like this I would set up my six-pounders just behind the crest of the hill with a good field of fire, placing my mortars forward and on the flanks to protect against encirclement."

"With a company of dragoons in reserve to give pursuit," added another.

A third officer shook his head. "Nay, I'd send my infantry in pursuit and let the dragoons swing wide to cut off the enemy retreat. That way you'd stand to get a nice bag of prisoners."

Henry listened closely, remembering every bit of instruction, every word of advice. He jotted down notes on the corners of maps, in the back of books and on sheets of scratch paper. He took down every scrap of information no matter how insignificant it might seem, storing it away for future use.

"But gentlemen," he said. "You speak in terms of companies and regiments. What about supplies and transportation, the movement of armies?"

The young officers threw back their heads with laughter. "So," one of them replied. "You would become a general. For that you must read Marshal Saxe and Vauban." He slapped Henry on the shoulder. "Come, gentlemen, let us be off. The lad has need of study. Who knows, someday we may be fighting under his command."

So once again Henry went back to his books. He read Saxe and Müller and studied the engineering methods of Vauban and Baron Von Coehoorn. He studied tactics, supply and the proper use of artillery, preparing himself for the day that he knew would soon come.

It was at about this time that Henry met with an accident which was to cause him lifelong embarrassment. He was hunting shore birds in the marshes around Noodles Island, on the outskirts of Boston, when his fowling piece accidentally went off, severing the two little fingers of his left hand. From that time on, he always wore a black silk handkerchief twined about his hand to conceal the defect.

One morning a short while later, while he was sitting in the back of the store going over the accounts, he noticed a pretty, dark-haired lass of eighteen or so standing between the rows of books. She was pleasingly plump with a small round face, full of charm and refinement. He watched her for a long while, wondering who she was. Many attractive young women were escorted into the shop by British officers or Tory squires, but this one seemed somehow different. She was alone, and she appeared to be bright and intelligent as she browsed from book to book.

A few minutes later she walked over and laid a small, leather-bound volume on the counter. Henry glanced at the title, Voltaire's *Life of Louis the Fourteenth.*

"A rather weighty tome for such a young Miss," he said with a chuckle.

She looked up and laughed, her dark eyes sparkling. "You don't approve?"

"On the contrary," said Henry. "Most young women would have selected a book of light verse or perhaps fiction."

"You mean romance?" she said.

Henry felt the heat of color rising in his cheeks as he handed her the wrapped book. She had almost reached the door when he called after her. "I'm sorry. I forgot your change."

She accepted it gracefully and backed away.

"Thank you, Miss."

"Miss Lucy," she said, making a small curtsy.

Henry lay awake till the wee hours of the morning daydreaming about Miss Lucy. He could think of nothing but that round, smiling face and those dark, laughing eyes, and he ardently hoped he would see them again soon.

The following morning he made a series of discreet inquiries and learned that this Miss Lucy was the daughter of the Honorable Thomas Flucker, Royal Secretary of the Massachusetts Bay Province. His heart sank with a resounding thud. Here was a comely lass whose charm and beauty were all that any man could ask for, yet as far as he was concerned she might as well have been a mythical princess on the mountains of the moon.

The Royal Secretary and his bevy of beautiful daughters lived in an aristocratic world of wealth and society. Loyal to their King and Tory to the core, they despised the rebel cause and looked upon tradesmen and merchants as little better than slaves. Inwardly Henry chided himself for even hoping that such a meeting could ever ripen into friendship.

But Henry reckoned without the courage of Miss Lucy, for she was a person of rare and unusual qualities, independent of thought and strong of will, with an abiding faith in her own convictions. She came to the store the following day and the day after that, and soon she and Henry were talking and chatting like old friends. They discussed books and art, history and science, and he found that she possessed a mind of remarkable ability and attainment. As time went on, they naturally turned to the subject of politics and Henry expounded on his views of the future, his love of country.

"This can be a great country," he said. "The greatest in the world. Just think of it, a vast land, still largely unexplored, filled with endless forests, wide flowing rivers and fertile valleys. Here is need for sawmills, foundries, shipyards, tanneries and dozens of other industries. It is a land of golden opportunity, I tell you." As he spoke, his eyes glowed with pride and hope for his vision of tomorrow. "But it cannot succeed and at the same time be stifled by unfair taxes; it cannot expand and still be

shackled by unreasonable restrictions. It's got to be free
—free to grow and to build, to work out a way of life of
its own."

Lucy looked up at him, thrilled and impressed by this
young man who could have such faith and vision in the
future.

And so, over the months, they met and talked and,
as was to be expected, they fell in love. Their romance
became the talk of Boston. It was poor boy, rich girl all
over again. It was whispered about in the coffeehouses
and the taverns and in the drawing rooms of the fashion-
able mansions throughout the city.

When the Honorable Thomas Flucker heard about it,
he flew into a rage. "Preposterous," he shouted. "Scan-
dalous. What will our friends think? Imagine my daughter
married to a common book salesman—and a rebel to
boot. I won't have it."

And while the Honorable Thomas' blood pressure continued to rise, Lucy went right on seeing her Henry.
"Papa has threatened to disown me," she said.

"Good," said Henry. "Then you'll be free to marry."

In the meantime, a new militia unit had been organized
in Boston and Henry was appointed second in command.
The unit was made up of tall, strapping young men from
the South End. Dressed in their splendid uniforms, they
made an inspiring sight as they marched down King Street
in holiday parades. With the drums beating and the fifes
playing, Henry marched at the head of his company while
Lucy stood on the sidelines, her heart bursting with pride.

The uneasy peace that began after the Boston Massacre
was short-lived. By 1774 new and more stringent taxes
were draining the colonies, and the people were again rising in open rebellion. Armed bands of Minutemen were

organized; angry patriots, disguised as Indians, dumped consignments of tea into Boston Harbor, and delegates from twelve of the thirteen colonies met in the first Continental Congress as England and America headed for a showdown.

From time to time mysterious figures were seen to visit Henry's store. They entered by a side door, carried on whispered conversations, then drifted out again as silently as they had come. One of them was a stocky young man with a limp. His name was Nathanael Greene, and he was an ex-Quaker and blacksmith from Rhode Island. Like Henry, he was interested in military subjects, and together they spent long hours studying maps and charts, indicating routes of march, marking out gun positions and strong points. It was all done in the spirit of exercise and practice, but there was an urgent intent to their seemingly harmless game.

Then, too, there was the tall, thin silversmith, Paul Revere, who frequently came in during the late hours of the evening, talking in quiet undertones about British troop movements, caches of arms and other bits of vital military information.

Henry committed no overt act of sedition or treason, but with all this coming and going and mysterious midnight visitors it wasn't long before his little shop aroused the suspicions of the British.

Certainly none of this weighed in Henry's favor in his courtship with Lucy. Her father was adamant as he warned her against the dire consequences of her folly. "You'll end up without a shilling," he stormed, "sleeping in a hovel, living on black bread and fish chowder while your sisters will enjoy the luxury of society—fine clothes, servants, wealth and respect."

"How can you say that, Papa," Lucy pleaded. "You don't even know him. If you'd talk to him, you'd see what a fine man he is."

"I know full well what kind of a man he is. He's a seditious malcontent taking advantage of your position, an unprincipled knave and little else, and I forbid him ever to set foot in this house."

"Then you refuse to bless our marriage?"

"Never," shouted the old man. "Never as long as I have strength enough to prevent it."

That night Lucy told Henry. "It's no use. Papa's still against it, more than ever now. But don't worry, we'll elope. We'll find a preacher and get married on our own. I'm eighteen now; they can't stop us."

"I've brought you to this," Henry said sadly.

"Nonsense. I'm a grown woman. I know what I want."

"Will you tell your father?"

"Yes. It may not make any difference, but at least he'll know we didn't run off behind his back."

But it did make a difference. When Thomas Flucker heard of it, it sent shivers of fear racing up and down his Tory spine. The shame and disgrace of an elopement was beyond thinking. Reluctantly he gave his consent, and the determined couple were married quietly and inconspicuously in June of 1774.

With William settled in a room of his own they set up housekeeping in Boston. Now that Henry was a part of the family, pressure was brought to bear to persuade him to give up his foolish notions.

It began a few weeks after they were married when a high-ranking British officer entered the shop and engaged him in conversation.

"You've a sound knowledge of artillery and engineering, Mr. Knox. Don't you think it might be time to put it to use?"

Henry smiled, gracious as always. "Not yet, Colonel, but perhaps soon."

The officer chuckled. "What I meant was that the Royal Artillery might have need for an ability such as yours. It would be a shame to see it go to waste."

"Oh it won't, sir. I can assure you of that."

"A commission might even be forthcoming, say in the rank of captain or major perhaps."

"My father-in-law is most generous."

The Colonel winced. "Come, Mr. Knox, let us not play games. You know as well as I do that commissions are purchased. Does it matter who pays the piper?"

"I happen to believe in freedom and independence," said Knox. "Your proposal leaves me neither."

A flush of anger was rising in the Colonel's face. "You have my offer, sir. I advise you to think it over."

"I have," said Henry. "And my answer is still no."

With that the officer turned on his heels and strode angrily out of the store.

Events moved swiftly now. Because of the uprisings and violence, the Port of Boston was closed. Nothing could go in or out without permission. General Gage, the new commander, set about fortifying the city. British troops were quartered in private homes, martial law was the order of the day and for all intents and purposes Boston became an occupied city. On September 1 a column of British troops marched on Charlestown and Cambridge, seizing cannons, powder and ammunition that rightfully belonged to the people. Tempers were at the breaking point, and the fateful hour was almost at hand.

In spite of a sharp decline in business, Henry continued

operating his little bookshop, and a few weeks later he was visited once again by the same British officer. This time the officer was accompanied by a young subaltern. Both men were stiff and formal as the Colonel reached into his pocket and took out an official-looking paper.

"I have the duty to inform you that you are under strict surveillance," he said, glaring at Knox with a cold, unfriendly stare. "You will go nowhere except to your shop or your home without the expressed permission of the British authorities. Is that clear?"

Henry nodded, dumbstruck, as the two officers started for the door. When they reached it, the Colonel turned. "And don't be foolish enough to try to leave Boston, Mr. Knox. You are being watched."

Henry stared after the two stiff-backed officers as they left the store. These were the same men he had mingled with, laughed with and entertained only a few months before. He watched as they disappeared down the street, cold and erect. "And now we are enemies," he thought. "All that remains is the shooting."

In the dark of night, at two o'clock in the morning of April 19, 1775, a strong force of British troops slipped out of Boston and made their way towards Concord to seize arms and ammunition being stored there by the patriots. Twenty hours later they returned—what remained of them—stumbling through the streets of Charlestown, a bleeding, wounded column of stragglers.

All day long the news had been trickling in, and Boston was tense with wonder. Henry Knox heard it like everyone else, through rumor, hearsay and gossip. The British had been routed by the Minutemen at Lexington and Concord and sent staggering back to Boston. England and the American Colonies were finally at war.

A few days later, shadowy figures with turned-up collars and hat brims tilted down over their eyes slipped in and out of Henry's store. There were hurried plans and whispered conversations, and that night Henry went home to Lucy.

"It's time to go," he said.

She looked up at him, her dark eyes wide with excitement. "I'm ready."

"You'll be safer here with your family and friends."

She shook her head firmly. "No, I want to go with you."

"You may never see them again."

"I knew that when I married you."

Hurriedly, they gathered up a few belongings—clothing, a bundle of private letters, keepsakes.

"What about the shop?" she asked.

"William will look after it," he said. "He'll be safe. They have no reason to suspect him."

They were about to leave when Lucy stopped. She went to the closet and took down Henry's militia sword encased in its long gilt scabbard.

"It's too risky," said Henry. "If they see that, we'll be held as prisoners."

"If they catch us, we'll be held anyway." Quickly she took off her skirt and with deft fingers sewed the weapon into the lining of her petticoat. When she had finished, she stood up.

"You look as innocent as a Tory," said Henry, smiling. "Come now, quickly, out the back way."

"Where are we going?"

"To Cambridge."

"Without horses?"

"I have friends," he said quietly.

Together they stepped out into the dark night, picking

their way through the orchard, Lucy holding up her skirts. A dog barked, and they stopped, breathlessly waiting. Then on they went again, with Henry feeling the excitement racing through his veins. At the end of the path a carriage was waiting.

An elderly man helped Lucy up, then handed the reins to Knox. "A mounted patrol just passed," he whispered. "Give them a few minutes to turn off at the crossroads, then go on. But watch for the sentry at the bridge. Now Godspeed and good luck."

Henry flicked the reins, and they started off, the horse's hooves clopping in the still night air. Lucy counted the minutes as they jogged along, trying to appear unhurried and nonchalant. With nervous fingers she traced the outline of the sword sewn in the lining of her petticoat, and she knew what it would mean if they were caught.

When they came to the bridge the sentry was in conversation with a woman. He started forward, then hesitated and, with a shrug of his shoulders, waved them on. They breathed a long sigh of relief and a half hour later came within sight of the towering spires of Harvard College. Henry drove the carriage through the winding streets to the headquarters of General Artemas Ward. They were rebels and patriots now, safe within the cordon of the American lines.

3

A HOT JULY SUN beat down on the dusty road as Henry Knox made his way towards Cambridge. In spite of his size he rode straight in the saddle, a warm glow of satisfaction on his plump, round face as he thought of the important work he had just accomplished.

With Lucy safe in Worcester, far removed from the dangers of war, he had volunteered his services, spending the past few months with Colonel Joseph Waters constructing breastworks and fortifications around Boston. These barricades and entrenchments would serve to keep the British penned up in their beleaguered stronghold and give the new American commander-in-chief, General George Washington, a chance to build an army out of a rabble of farmers, blacksmiths and shopkeepers.

Henry had worked hard, throwing himself into his task with energy and enthusiasm. Busy with this, he had missed the gallant stand at Bunker Hill. But now the British were licking their wounds, and the rebels had time to conceal their woeful shortage of arms and ammunition, time to build up strength and to think about the crazy, impossible war they had got themselves into. Like wet, bedraggled puppies nipping at the heels of a hungry lion, they little realized that their chances of victory were pitifully slim.

But Henry was not discouraged. He was a patriot and

a soldier—a soldier without a uniform, without even a commission. He had learned his art of warfare from the pages of a book, and all he asked was a chance to serve his country in the best way that he knew.

Now, as he made his way down the road to Cambridge, he saw a pair of riders coming in the opposite direction. They were still at a distance, but they were riding at a brisk canter and it wasn't long before he could make out the thin ramrod figure of General Charles Lee. The other rider was a tall, aristocratic-looking gentleman wearing a dark blue and buff officer's uniform. His manner was genial but aloof, and he had an air of quiet, restrained authority.

Lee greeted Knox with a perfunctory nod then introduced the new commander-in-chief, General George Washington.

The big man smiled, his blue eyes showing a depth of warmth and understanding that belied his stern appearance. "General Lee tells me the work at Roxbury is almost complete."

Henry beamed. "Yes, sir. The abutments and entrenchments are constructed in parallel lines overlooking Boston Neck, and the troops are already in position."

Washington nodded. "We are fortunate in having a man of your ability, Mr. Knox. At the moment our need for men with a knowledge of artillery and engineering is most urgent."

"I am honored to be of service," said Henry.

Lee interrupted. "We now have a solid ring of siege works around the city. The British will think twice before trying to force their way out."

Washington continued looking at Henry, all but ignoring Lee's comment. "Perhaps Mr. Knox would be good enough to accompany us back to Roxbury. I should like to see these defenses."

Henry was startled by the unexpected invitation. Coming from a man of such importance, this was a distinct honor. Quickly he swung his horse around, riding side by side with the commander-in-chief, his boyish heart swelling with pride.

High on the slopes of Roxbury heights, overlooking Boston, Knox showed Washington the fortifications and breastworks. He indicated the best positions for cannons and mortars and the vantage points from which they would have the best field of fire. He conducted the generals on a tour of the parallel bunkers and trenches, pointing out the importance of their location and how they would serve as a second line of defense in case of an attack.

Washington was concerned by the acute shortage of siege guns but considerably impressed with the military acumen of the earthworks. He listened attentively, nodding his head in agreement, making an occasional comment to Lee. Then he pointed to the harbor, where a dozen British ships rode at anchor. "And what about those British frigates?" he asked. "If they move in closer, they could make it a bit uncomfortable for you up here."

Henry laughed. "We have the advantage, sir. They can raise their guns to heaven, but they'll never reach our lines. On the other hand, if they come too close we can blast them out of the water."

"If you had the cannons."

"Yes, sir," said Henry soberly. "If we only had the cannons." Then, as an afterthought, he added: "Fortunately the enemy seems to think we have."

Washington smiled with amused understanding. There

was something about this fat, jovial lad that he liked. Maybe it was the deep, rolling tenor of his laugh or the unwavering mood of boyish optimism. Whatever it was, it was a welcome change from the atmosphere of gloom and discontent that had surrounded him these past few weeks.

When they had finished their tour of inspection they started back for Cambridge. They rode in silence for a while, but as they neared the encampment Washington turned to Henry. "You have done an excellent job, Mr. Knox. Your understanding of artillery and siege construction is most valuable. I trust we can count on you for continued help during these trying times?"

"I should be pleased to serve in whatever capacity my ability and background will allow."

"Then I would be obliged if you will call on me at my headquarters," said the General. "I have some thoughts on the organization of our artillery that I believe might interest you."

Henry was jubilant. That night he dashed off a letter to Lucy telling her of his meeting with the great man. "He is a splendid officer and carries himself with ease and dignity. It would be a rare distinction to serve under his command."

A few days later Henry presented himself at Washington's headquarters. He was admitted by an aide and ushered into the General's study. The big man got up to greet him, holding out his hand. "Thank you for coming, Mr. Knox." He said it with respect and sincerity, and Henry's heart filled with admiration.

Yet, in spite of his broad smile, Knox could see the fatigue and frustration in Washington's eyes. He knew the trouble he was having trying to make an army out of an undisciplined mob, smooth over sectional feuds, cajole provisions and supplies out of a hesitant Congress and present an appearance of strength and unity when all about him was chaos, jealousy and confusion.

But if it showed in his eyes, it was not noticeable in his voice. He spoke in his usual quiet manner. "I trust you will not consider me presumptuous, Mr. Knox, but I have taken the liberty of putting your name before Congress for a commission."

Knox was pleased. It was exactly what he had hoped for. "I am deeply honored," he said. "And I will be willing to lend my weight to whatever task may further the cause." As he said the words, Henry looked down at his portly figure and caught the unwitting humor of his remark.

The General caught it too and tried to stifle a smile. "I am sure you will," he said. "And I am just as certain that your wit and buoyancy will lighten your burdens along the way."

Both men laughed heartily, and Washington again experienced a feeling of relief and satisfaction in the company of this jovial young man. He asked him about his family and his interest in books and military subjects. Then the talk turned to the war and the prospects for the future. As always, Henry's outlook was hopeful and optimistic. He had a firm belief in the righteousness of their cause and felt certain of victory.

"Yes, we can win," Washington agreed, "if we can turn this unruly mob into an army, if we can teach them a semblance of order and discipline."

"For that we will need capable officers," said Henry.

"That is exactly why I asked you here. You have ability,

judgment and a sound knowledge of military engineering. At the moment we are sadly lacking in this vital area."

Washington's tone was grave, and Henry sensed an urgent purpose as the General turned and looked him straight in the eye. "How would you like to serve as my chief of artillery?"

Henry Knox was stunned. He had expected a commission, perhaps a place on the staff, but this was beyond his wildest dreams. Command of the entire artillery—it was incredible. He hardly knew what to say.

"Colonel Gridley now holds that position," said Washington. "But he has served his country long and well, and now he is not in the best of health. I am sure he would be pleased if you would accept the post."

Knox was silent for a moment, trying to compose his thoughts. It was a momentous occasion in his young life, and he wanted to accept with the proper amount of respect and decorum—he wanted to say the right thing. "It is indeed a great honor, sir, and I will do my best to serve with courage and distinction." Then he blurted out, "But, begging your pardon, sir. Where is the artillery I am to command?" As soon as the words were out he knew he had done it again.

Washington grinned. This young man had an amazing knack for hitting on the preposterous. "You are right. We have only a few brass fieldpieces, some mortars and howitzers. If we hope to drive the British out of Boston, we are going to need more than that."

"I shall inspect our weapons and draw up a list immediately," said Knox.

"I am afraid it will not be very long," said Washington, shaking his head. "But somehow, somewhere, we will have to find more."

"Perhaps we can, sir. I understand there are dozens of good cannons up at Fort Ticonderoga. With your permission they could be brought down here to strengthen our lines."

The General looked up quickly. This was the kind of thinking he liked—imaginative and expedient. His thoughts flew up to Ticonderoga, and in his mind's eye he saw the heavy cannons, some of them weighing over five thousand pounds apiece. Then he thought of the three hundred miles of trackless wilderness over which they would have to be hauled. And here was this bold young man talking as though he were suggesting carrying an armload of muskets across a village green. Yet this reckless youth might succeed where a cautious older man would hesitate.

"You think it can be done?"

"I'm sure of it, sir."

Washington's voice had a new ring of hope. "It might be just the thing to turn the trick." He was talking half aloud, thinking to himself. Then he looked directly at Henry. "I'll present your plan to Congress for immediate action. If they agree, the mission is yours."

But the wheels of Congress turned slowly, and it was November before Knox started out on his long journey. Accompanied by his brother William, now eighteen, he went first to New York. Then they started north, riding hard, making forty miles a day.

When they reached the lower end of Lake George the weather was cold and blustery, and Knox decided to put up for the night before making the long boat trip to

Ticonderoga. The bunk houses and hostels were full, but he managed to find a small one-room cabin near the side of the road. He had not been sleeping long when he was awakened by the sound of someone moving about in the room. By the flickering light of the fire he could make out the figure of a man making up his bed. The stranger had already taken off his coat and boots and was crawling between the blankets when he noticed that Henry was awake.

"I am sorry, sir." His voice was quiet and refined. "I had hoped to bed down without disturbing you. If you will forgive me I shall try to be more careful."

Henry was curious. It wasn't often that one met an educated man in these backwoods areas, and this voice had the decided ring of a gentleman. He looked up and saw the stranger's face outlined in the dim light. He was a youth in his early twenties with sharp, clean-cut features and an olive complexion, easily the most handsome young man that Henry had ever met.

"It's a bad night for traveling," Henry offered.

"Yes," the young man agreed. "I've just come down the lake. I was lucky to get this far before dark."

Henry nodded, glancing about the room. "Not much of a lodging, but at least we've got a warm fire."

The stranger reached into his knapsack, fumbling about for a moment. "And a book or two," he said, holding out a small, leather-bound volume, "if you'd care to read."

Henry took the book, turning it over in his hands to read the title. "Ah yes, *The Deserted Village.*"

"One of my favorites," said the stranger. "Are you interested in literature?"

"I was a bookseller before the war."

"Then you are familiar with Goldsmith?"

"Yes, and Cervantes and Voltaire and Defoe," added Henry.

Far into the night the two men discussed books and literature, art and philosophy. Each was fascinated by the other's knowledge of history and events. They were kindred spirits with comparable backgrounds and similar interests.

From his knapsack the young man took out still another book. It was a bound journal filled with jottings and sketches.

"I've been keeping a sort of diary," he explained. "Impressions of all the places I've been to in Canada and America, people, customs, scenery—anything that strikes my fancy."

Henry leafed through the pages intrigued by the clever drawings of Indians, woodsmen, animals and birds. The margins were filled with notes describing landscapes and natural wonders, the daily habits and dress of the natives.

During the long conversation Henry learned that the young man could also speak several languages. He had traveled extensively in Europe, and he displayed a wide knowledge of commerce, government and military history. His wit, his charm and personality made a lasting impression on the young artilleryman.

They talked until the early hours of the morning, when finally, tired and exhausted, they fell asleep. It seemed barely minutes before Henry was aroused by the bright sunlight streaming through the windows. His young friend was already awake, pulling on his boots and picking up his belongings.

Henry dressed quickly. He had just finished packing his gear and turned to say good-bye when the sight that met his eyes made him stop in shocked surprise.

The young man was standing there impeccably dressed in the uniform of a British officer. From his powdered white wig and scarlet coat to his shiny black boots he was every inch the soldier. He smiled graciously at Henry's confusion. "Lieutenant John André of the British 7th Regiment at your service, sir."

Recovering from his initial surprise Knox stammered, "You are a prisoner of war?"

"Yes," said André. "Captured at Fort Chambly."

"And so we are enemies," said Knox.

"Not really, sir, only by circumstance. By all other counts we are friends."

"And where do you go from here?"

"To Lancaster, Pennsylvania—hopefully to be exchanged."

"I wish it were otherwise."

André smiled. "Then let us hope that someday we shall meet again under different circumstances."

As Henry stood there watching the young officer march off down the road, he little realized how soon that wish was destined to come true.

A few hours later Knox was sailing up the length of Lake George. Impressed by André's journal, he now began a diary of his own, jotting down all the sights and events that came to him on his adventurous journey.

Just before dark he came in sight of the high gray walls of Fort Ticonderoga. Here, atop the parapets and watchtowers of the great fort, were the huge cannons, the eighteen- and twenty-four-pounders, the ponderous howitzers and squat Dutch mortars. He looked up at them trying to assess the difficulties that would have to be overcome to get the heavy guns back to Cambridge. At first glance it looked almost impossible. But Henry Knox was young, only twenty-five. He smiled at difficulties and laughed in the face of the impossible. Had he been aware of the delays and obstacles that lay in his path, he might have given up before he began.

4

THE GREAT FORT WAS SET in an area of wild, scenic beauty. Its sturdy bastions of stone and masonry were surrounded by mountains of pine forests sweeping down to the glittering waters of Lake Champlain. High on its ramparts and battlements were the big guns jutting out through the casements like black fingers of defiance. There were cannons and howitzers and mortars, some of them laying about, damaged beyond repair. Many cannons in excellent condition waited only for cannoneers and ramrods to put them back into action.

Henry Knox inspected them carefully, selecting fifty-nine of the best pieces. They ranged in size from nine- to twenty-four-pounders, the largest measuring eleven feet over all. By use of block and tackle they were hoisted over the battlements and lowered to the ground. Soldiers and civilians from the local garrison rolled them onto stone-boats, and teams of husky draft animals dragged them across the neck of land to the head of Lake George, where they were loaded aboard a huge barge.

Laden down with sixty tons of artillery and twenty-three boxes of lead and a barrel of flints, the big scowlike vessel barely floated above the surface of the water. It moved out slowly, accompanied by two smaller boats, a pettianger and a battoe, and the strange flotilla started its precarious voyage down the forty-mile passage to Fort George. Brawny-armed boatmen manned the sweeps, pushing the clumsy craft through the water. At first all went well, but on the second day out a strong head-wind came up from the south, tossing the smaller boats about and all but swamping the barge. Desperately the men fought against the gale, struggling at the oars, but it was no use. After five hours of futile effort they gave up and pulled into Sabbath Day Point, where they fell to the ground, cold, hungry and completely exhausted.

The next day they started out again, still fighting against the icy winds. To save time Knox went on ahead in the pettianger, leaving William in charge of the scow. Rowing hard, he reached Fort George before nightfall and began making arrangements for the land portion of the journey. Now the surrounding wilderness echoed to the rasping sound of saws and the bang of hammers as eighty-two heavy wooden sleds were constructed. Big, barrel-chested oxen and sturdy workhorses were brought in from the local farms and settlements, and soon all was in readiness.

But, as the time passed and the scow failed to make its appearance, Knox became worried. He paced up and down the shore, gazing out across the water, waiting impatiently. Finally he sent a boat out to investigate. The report that came back was beyond his worst expectations. The scow, with its entire cargo of artillery, had been swamped and sunk off Sabbath Day Point.

Knox was stunned. The expedition that had started out with such glowing hopes was already a total failure. Bitterly disappointed, he was getting ready to start back for the Point when a messenger arrived with a letter from William. The first report had been correct but grossly exaggerated. The scow had sunk in shallow water. By loading some of the cannons into the lighter craft and bailing out the sunken barge William had managed to get it afloat. Two days later it arrived at Fort George, not a single gun missing.

Here the cannons and mortars were loaded onto the waiting sleds, the carriage wheels, canisters and ramrods lashed on top. The snorting oxen and skittish workhorses were hitched into place, and the long overland trek began. To the echoing crack of bullwhips and the bellowing shouts of teamsters the strange convoy wound its way through the silent, snow-covered forests. It would pass over three hundred miles of wilderness, including many places where there were no roads or trails.

Animals and men struggled up the steep inclines, their warm breath condensing on the chill morning air. Teamsters and soldiers bundled against the biting cold, heads down, driving their charges on. The convoy stretched out for miles with its unwieldy cargo of artillery, the sleds creaking under the heavy loads.

Mounted on a fine chestnut mare, Knox plowed through the snow. He ranged ahead to reconnoiter the trail or rode back to lend a hand with a bogged-down sled. He went up and down the line, cheering the men, spurring them on with his constant display of energy and enthusiasm.

But the going was agonizingly slow. Sleds broke down, frightened animals refused to pull. Oxen slipped on the icy trails or floundered helplessly in the deep snow. Hours were lost getting them back into the traces, and sometimes it took an entire day to plod two weary miles.

On Christmas Eve they reached Saratoga, with over two hundred miles yet to go. It began to snow, a thick, heavy downfall continuing all that night and far into the next day. Trails vanished, oxen and horses sank up to their bellies in snow. Christmas Day found them plodding wearily along, struggling through the swirling drifts.

In spite of the weather Knox sent a message to Washington with his usual display of optimism. "Within sixteen or seventeen days I hope, with the help of God, to present you with a noble train of artillery." He wrote to Lucy telling her he would be home within three weeks. It was clear he had little idea of the difficulties that still lay ahead.

Coming down along the west bank of the Hudson the convoy passed through villages and hamlets where the good burghers came out to view the strange procession. They gathered by the hundreds from farms and homesteads to stare in amazement at the big guns, to run their hands over the long, smooth barrels of the cannons and to poke astonished faces into the gaping maws of the stubby mortars. They danced and sang, and they plied the teamsters with biscuits, rum and cider. At times it seemed like a hilarious winter carnival, and fun-loving, jovial Henry Knox enjoyed it right along with the men. He had the support of the entire community now, and even the area commander, old General Phillip Schyler, helped pave the way, arranging for provisions and supplies and hiring fresh teams of oxen.

At Lansing's Ferry they found the Hudson frozen over and decided to try a crossing. They sent a large eighteen-pounder across first, pulled by a team of horses at the end of a forty-foot rope. A man walked along beside the gun, a hatchet in his hand ready to cut the line if necessary. Half way across the ice cracked, echoing in the still air. The hatchet flashed in the sunlight, severing the rope, and the noble eighteen sank beneath the water.

Knox heard the news just as he was sitting down to dinner at General Schyler's house some thirty miles away. He jumped up from the table and rode hard for Lansing's Ferry, arriving there angry and out of breath. He saw the jagged hole in the ice where the cannon had crashed through, and he saw the young lieutenant standing there, embarrassed and dejected.

"What's the matter with you, man?" Knox's voice boomed out on the cold night air. "Didn't you have sense enough to test the ice?" He pointed a finger at the gaping hole. "It's barely thick enough to hold your weight. What did you expect?"

Then he saw the long rope laying on the ice, trailing off into the depths, and the faint flicker of a smile crossed his face. "The rope," he said, "it's still attached?"

"Yes, sir," said the Lieutenant hopefully.

Henry looked about quickly, examining the cracks in the ice, gauging the distance. He spoke quietly now, his anger completely gone. "Have a long timber placed across the hole, Lieutenant. Let your rope pay over it in the direction of the far shore. Hitch up your team and pull. When your gun comes to the surface snag it around the muzzle and have another team ready to pull it out."

The men were moving now, getting the timbers ready, leading the teams into place. Knox bellowed the orders. "All right, pull away. Slowly now, keep it going. Here she comes, Lieutenant. Ready with your ropes. Now tie in with your second team. More timbers. That's right, haul away. Easy now, bring her across easy."

It was all done in a matter of minutes, precisely and efficiently, and the men looked at this bulky young engineer with new respect, a gleam of admiration shining in their eyes.

They reached Albany on January 4, 1776, many weeks behind schedule. Unfortunately a freak midwinter thaw had set in, turning the frozen Hudson into slush puddles of water. It brought the convoy to a complete halt, frustrating drivers and officers alike.

But Henry Knox was not the kind of man to sit and wait. He had the men cut huge holes in the ice, hoping the overflow of water would freeze during the night to add strength to the soft ice. It worked. A few days later a freeze came, making his ice bridge solid and strong.

Now the citizens of Albany turned out in force to lend a hand. It was another gala occasion as they tugged and pulled, vying with each other to get the guns across.

At Claverack the convoy made a sharp turn directly east, starting through the narrow, thickly wooded passes of the Berkshires. There were no roads now, not even trails. The winter landscape was one of spectacular beauty. Great blankets of snow covered the slopes and weighed down the branches of the evergreens. Tall stands of pine and spruce trees grew close, towering into the sky, while huge areas of hemlock and mountain laurel were interspersed with enormous boulders and rotting windfalls. Slowly the long convoy wormed its way along the ravines and defiles. The oxen stumbled and horses shied as teamsters pulled and shouted, guiding them through.

Then they came to East Otis, a place of steep chasms and sheer drops hundreds of feet down, covered with glazed ice and snow. It was the most difficult passage of the entire expedition. Men and cattle balked. These men were teamsters. They knew the capacity of their animals, and what they were asked to do now was utterly impossible. Oxen were strong, dependable beasts, but they were not mountain goats. Nor did they have wings.

Knox looked down those rugged hundred-foot drops that were covered with ice. He saw the steep ravines and canyons separated by rivers and swamps, and he knew how the men must have felt. Still he would not give up. They had come too far.

He called them together in a clearing of the forest, the soldiers and teamsters, the men in buckskin and homespun. They sat on the sleds and leaned against the big howitzers, red-eyed and weary. He saw the bold, sullen expression of defiance on their faces, and he knew it would not be easy. He started by telling them how much they had accomplished and how proud their country was of their courage and endurance.

"The enemy is waiting," he shouted, his deep voice rolling through the treetops, "waiting to take away our freedom—nay, our very lives. But here we have the means to drive him from our land. You and I can win this battle. This much, this page of history, lies within our grasp. If we can get these guns through to General Washington, I promise you we can drive the British out of Boston."

He looked around at the scattered group of faces, these farmers and frontiersmen, standing silent and proud, this thing taunting them—hating to give it up, yet confused and uncertain.

A burly teamster stepped forward. "That valley lies over a thousand feet below," he said. "Where are the roads, where are the trails?"

"We will make our own trails," cried Knox, "carve

out our own roads if necessary. It will not be easy, but I tell you, it can be done."

For three hours he talked to them, pleading with them to stick by him. He alone, he said, would take full responsibility for every yoke of oxen, every piece of equipment. He would personally supervise the dangerous descent every step of the way. Each team, each man, would be helped by all the others. They could go as slowly as they liked, use every trick, every safety device. Once through the pass they would be free to leave, their job done.

When he had finished he looked around, trying to gauge the temper of these laconic New Englanders, trying to read the answer in their dull, listless eyes.

"What do you say?" he shouted. "Do we have the spunk to go the last hundred miles? Do we show them what we are made of, or do we quit and hand our country over to the enemy?" In the dark silence of the evergreen forests he waited for his answer. But all he heard was the soft whisper of the wind in the pine boughs.

Then his great, thundering voice boomed out once more in angry frustration. "Well, speak up. Do we quit or do we go on?"

A low murmur went through the crowd. They began to move now, mumbling to one another, nodding their heads. Slowly they rubbed the sleep from their tired eyes and shook the weariness from their shoulders. They went back to their teams and started down those slick, ice-covered passes one sled at a time. They used drag chains and cinch ropes, hitching them around the sturdy pines, letting the heavy loads down foot by foot. Drivers jammed logs under sled runners to keep them from running over the animals. It was cruel, back-breaking work, fighting gravity all the way, and Henry Knox pitched in, lending a hand, shouting orders, taking the worst of it right along with the men.

For six long days and nights the towering forests were filled with the sounds of bawling cattle and the shouts of teamsters as the ponderous guns were eased down the steep, ice-covered chasms, dropping a distance of almost fifteen hundred feet within five miles. Yet slowly, doggedly, the incredible task was done, and the weary procession stumbled out of the green darkness into the light of the valley.

Here Henry paid the men off. With tears in his eyes he thanked each one of them and sent them back to their homes. Then, hiring new teamsters with fresh spans of oxen, he began the final leg of his journey to Cambridge.

All along the route now people lined up to see the wondrous caravan. It was a triumphant occasion, and Henry Knox was human enough to enjoy the cheers and acclaim. He was proud of his unique convoy of artillery and prouder still of the small band of men who had made it all possible. At Westfield the villagers staged an impromptu celebration, and Henry had his cannoneers set up the biggest mortar of the lot, a squat, barrel-like weapon nicknamed "The Old Sow." They rammed it full of powder and set it off. With a thundering blast it belched forth a column of smoke and flame, shaking the surrounding foothills, an ominous warning to the British Redcoats holed up in Boston.

From Westfield they made their way toward Cambridge. Most of the mountainous terrain was behind them, and the convoy traveled on level ground. Yet the going could still be difficult. Midwinter thaws melted the snow, turning the dirt roads into quagmires of mud and slush. But slowly the distance closed, and the ponderous caravan neared its goal.

It was an impossible task, but it had been done—done by a man who was too much of a boy to believe in the impossible, too inexperienced to know when he was licked and too foolhardly to know when to quit.

On January 23, 1776, the weary, mud-begrimed convoy trudged into Framingham, a scant twenty miles from Cambridge. Here Knox deposited most of the heavier guns, taking the six- and nine-pounders along with him to Cambridge. At headquarters he was greeted with a resounding ovation as he presented his commander-in-chief with his noble train of artillery. Washington was elated and welcomed the young artilleryman with open arms. But the commander-in-chief had some good news of his own. While Henry was away the patriots had captured the British brigantine *Nancy,* complete with cargo and thousands of rounds of cannon shot that would fit nicely into the guns from Ticonderoga.

By now Congress had approved Henry's commission, and he was able to write another one of his enthusiastic letters to Lucy, telling her about the good news. He had been appointed to the rank of full colonel in complete command of the growing American artillery.

5

WASHINGTON HUNCHED OVER HIS MAP, his big finger tracing a half circle around the beleaguered city of Boston. Now that he had the guns from Ticonderoga, now that his army was stronger and better disciplined than it was when he had first arrived, he was ready to strike his first blow for freedom. But he would have to act fast. The enemy would not stay penned up much longer. Any day now British transports might heave into sight, bringing reinforcements and supplies. Then it would be too late.

At first he thought of moving out in a bold attack across the frozen harbor, but his generals had warned against it. Now, as he studied the map with its contours of outlying hills, he knew what he had to do. Carefully he laid his plans, realizing that if they were to succeed they would have to be executed swiftly and without delay.

Young Henry Knox was to play an important role in this daring scheme. On the night of March 2, 1776, he ordered his artillery batteries into position. Huge thirteen-inch mortars, together with howitzers and eighteen-pounders, were set up on Lechmere's Point, Cobble Hill and Roxbury. Knox personally supervised their placement, checking for range and elevation. Then all was ready. As the sky darkened into night he gave the order. Like a rolling crash of thunder the guns opened fire, pounding the enemy positions within the city. The bombardment could be heard for miles around. Sentries walking their posts felt the earth tremble beneath their feet. Sailors on watch in the harbor saw the western sky light up with brilliant flashes of muzzle fire, and citizens waiting in their homes were shaken by the heavy blasts. One and all, they knew it for what it was—the next round in the desperate fight for freedom had begun.

For three long nights the pounding continued, with the enemy answering round for round. Then, on the evening of March 4, Knox increased the tempo, firing his big guns as quickly as they could be reloaded.

But all this din and uproar was only a diversion. Seven miles away, under the cover of darkness, 2,000 men and 360 oxcarts were hauling entrenching tools, cannon shot and the big guns from Ticonderoga up the heights of Dorchester. Hour after hour they labored, digging earthworks, constructing fortifications reinforced with timber, bales of hay and facings of tightly bound saplings. Axmen cut sharply pointed stakes from the nearby orchards, driving them into the ground in front of the trenches. Hundreds of empty wine barrels were filled with earth and rocks and chained together to be rolled down the steep incline in the face of the advancing foe. The creaking oxcarts emptied their loads of timber, their kegs of powder and boxes of cannon shot, then went down the hill for more.

All night long the work continued without letup. When the men became tired they were replaced by fresh crews who enlarged the entrenchments, making them strong and impregnable. The ringing sound of the picks and shovels was drowned out by the steady boom of Knox's cannons, and a low overhanging mist concealed the busy preparations. By early dawn the work was done. The new defenses were armed, fully manned and ready.

The next morning General Howe looked up and rubbed his eyes in incredulous disbelief. He was staring up into the threatening maws of big eighteen- and twenty-four-pounders, facing a position infinitely stronger than the one he had encountered at Bunker Hill. The thought of this new menace, coupled with the memory of the old one, made him wince. "The rebels have done more in one night," said Howe, "than my entire army could have done in a month." His officers and men looked up at the bristling guns of Dorchester Heights and agreed.

Howe realized that his position was untenable. His own guns could not be elevated high enough to reach the rebel lines; yet his every position, even the ships in the harbor, was now vulnerable to enemy fire. To save face he ordered an attack, but secretly he made plans to evacuate. A violent storm aborted the impending attack, and preparations for the evacuation were immediately begun.

Fortunately the city of Boston was not put to the torch as the rebels expected, but it was plundered. For days the British roamed the streets, breaking into stores and warehouses, carrying off shoes, foodstuffs, clothing and other commodities. Anything that might prove useful or of comfort to the enemy was hastily carted off and loaded aboard the waiting transports.

The Tories, who had collaborated with the British, now feared for their lives. They knew that as soon as the British left they would be harshly treated and they pleaded with Howe to be taken along. Howe supplied them with ships, but they had to provide their own deckhands and crews. It was a sorry plight for the hundreds of men, women and children who crowded aboard the small vessels. Most of them were people of wealth, used to comfort and fine living. Now they were compelled to huddle together in crowded quarters, thirty or forty to a cabin, sleeping on deck or in the passageways, wherever they could find a vacant spot, surviving as best they could.

On March 17 the last of Howe's rear-guard units climbed aboard the ships and the British fleet sailed quietly away. As Henry Knox had promised, the big guns of Ticonderoga had helped drive the enemy out of Boston. The bill for his Ticonderoga expedition was $2,500, perhaps the cheapest military victory in history.

A few days later the patriot army entered the liberated city, and Colonel Henry Knox rode proudly at the head of the column beside his commander-in-chief. For the twenty-five-year-old bookseller it was a glorious homecoming. He had left, almost a year ago, as an enemy fugitive, hunted and despised. He was returning now a conquering hero.

But his initial feelings of elation were soon tempered by less happy tidings. He found his bookshop in Cornhill ransacked and looted. Hundreds of books, maps and periodicals were missing, and an entire inventory of stationery and supplies was gone. All that remained was a useless mess of torn litter and broken furniture. It made his heart ache to see his once beautiful store so desecrated. He learned too that Lucy's family—her mother, father and sisters—had all sailed off with the fleeing Tories, perhaps never to return. It would be sad news to bring home to his waiting wife.

But although the enemy had carted off much of the clothing and foodstuffs, they had foolishly left behind great quantities of military supplies. Thousands of blankets were found abandoned on the wharf, along with

medical supplies and military stores. Hundreds of cavalry
and artillery horses were left grazing in the surrounding
hills because there was no room for them aboard the
crowded transports.

Most of all Henry Knox gloated over the great number
of guns and the hundreds of rounds of cannon shot and
mortar shells abandoned by the fleeing enemy. There were
sixty-nine fieldpieces in all, many of them in excellent
condition, others spiked so hurriedly that it would take
only a few minutes for blacksmiths to get them back into
action. To Knox it was the greatest coup of the campaign,
adding badly needed guns to his growing collection of
artillery.

Yet even with Boston secure and the battle won, Washington did not rejoice. He had no illusions about an easy
victory. He knew the British would be back and that the
most likely place for their return would be the port of
New York. Centrally located, with excellent harbor facilities, it was the one place on the coast ideally situated to
drive a wedge between the colonies. With this threat in
mind Washington hurriedly sent his army down the coast
to fortify and hold the City of New York.

Colonel Knox was ordered to follow with his train of
artillery, stopping off at Rhode Island and Connecticut
to set up coastal defenses against possible enemy raids.
Lucy accompanied him as far as Fairfield, Connecticut.
Here she went into confinement to give birth to their first
child. It was a girl, and they christened her Lucy after her
mother.

In New York, Henry worked tirelessly, planning fortifications and setting up coastal defenses along the river
front and landing places. Batteries of cannons were put
into position at Kips Bay and Hell Gate; trenches and

breastworks were dug all along the vital areas of approach in Manhattan and Long Island. After months of preparation he reported one hundred and twenty-one guns in place and ready for action. He wrote to his brother William, who had waited until the Britsh evacuated Boston, then returned to that city to re-establish the shattered bookstore. "If General Howe comes up like a man and brings his ships before our batteries there will be the finest fight that ever was seen for we shall be able to bring a great number of cannons to bear on his ships at once." It was an empty boast and one that he would soon have cause to regret.

A month later Lucy arrived with the baby. They lived in Henry's spacious headquarters at number one Broadway, overlooking the harbor. They were a happy family, but as the months passed, Henry became anxious for the safety of his wife and child.

"You should be going back to Connecticut," he urged. "The enemy may show up at any time now, and you'll be caught here without means of escape."

Lucy chuckled brightly. "The enemy, that's all anyone ever talks about. It's been three months now, and we haven't seen a single Redcoat. If it's safe enough for Martha Washington, it's safe enough for me."

Henry shook his head in resignation. It was true that General Washington's wife was here in New York, but that didn't mean the danger had passed. "In Philadelphia there's word that Howe has already left Halifax with a fleet of transports," he warned. "They could be here at almost any time."

"Rumors," said Lucy, cooing softly to the baby. "I've been hearing stories about Howe and his warships ever since I got here. He's probably gone back to England and forgotten all about the war. He'd be smart if he did. It's nothing but a lot of foolish nonsense anyway."

Henry smiled in spite of himself. Lucy had a way of making the most serious events appear trivial and unimportant. At heart she was still a gay and blithesome child and saw no reason why worldly events should interfere with her happiness. Perhaps this was one of the reasons why he loved her. To her the war was merely a bothersome inconvenience that kept her separated from her husband. If she had her way she would call the whole thing off and invite everyone, friend and foe alike, to a gala celebration. It was as simple as that.

Henry patted the baby on the head affectionately, shrugged his shoulders and went back to writing out his orders.

A few days later, on the bright Sunday morning of June 25, 1776, the little family sat down to breakfast. Their window overlooked the bay, and Lucy could see the glistening waters of the harbor, with the green rolling hills of New Jersey in the distance. The fragrance of blooming wisteria drifted in on the cool morning air, and everything seemed tranquil and serene. They ate quietly, completely content in each other's company, their little world peaceful and undisturbed.

Suddenly, as Lucy stared out the window, Henry saw her body stiffen with fright. Quickly he followed her gaze. Far away on the horizon he could make out three British men-of-war sailing up the bay. It was the vanguard of the British army. The enemy had finally come. All over the city, flags were hoisted, cannons boomed and alarm guns were sounded as soldiers and horsemen raced through the streets, heading for their stations.

Henry jumped up from the table stammering with excitement, rushing about, packing clothes and blankets, while Lucy dressed the baby. He gathered her luggage together, all the while shouting over his shoulder, "I told you this would happen. Now what are we to do? Every carriage in the city will be commandeered."

She looked at him in desperation. They were both on edge now, irritable with fear. "You're a staff officer," she said. "Surely you have some influence."

Henry winced. "Last week—yesterday, maybe. But now I don't know. I'll be lucky if I can get a horse." He raced out into the street, the perspiration running down his forehead. He was back in twenty minutes with a dilapidated carriage waiting at the door. "Quickly," he said. "Are you ready?"

She came out carrying the baby while the driver, an old man, put her bags in the back. Henry helped her up and kissed her lightly on the cheek.

She looked at him with surprise. "You're not coming?" she asked.

Henry gasped. "Woman, I have a war to fight." He motioned toward the harbor. "Do you suppose they will wait while I see my wife to safety?"

"War," she snorted, "that's all you men think about." She saw the hurt in his eyes and quickly her frown changed to a smile. "I'm sorry," she said. "I didn't mean that. Please be careful, and let me know when I can be with you again. It will seem so long."

He patted her hand. "The driver will take you to Kings Bridge. From there you should be able to get a coach. Write as soon as you get home and let me know how things are." He kissed her again, then watched as the carriage drove off into the distance.

But the enemy did not invade New York that day or the next. Instead they began a slow, steady buildup of men and materials. A massive armada of one hundred and thirty ships sailed into the bay, dropping anchor off Staten Island. Composed of frigates, transports, supply ships and men-of-war, it was an awe-inspiring sight. But this was not all. A few days later another one hundred and fifty vessels came into view bearing thousands of Redcoats, Hessians and dragoons complete with equipment, horses and artillery. Day after day the ships continued to arrive until the harbor was a forest of masts, yardarms and spars.

But although the odds seemed overwhelming, Henry Knox and most of his compatriots were not discouraged. They had an abiding faith in their cause and a superb confidence in their fighting ability. And now, as if to buoy up those hopes, they suddenly received the exhilarating news that the Declaration of Independence had recently been signed in Philadelphia. On July 10 it was formally announced to the troops. Bells rang, cannons boomed and great bonfires lit up the night. Even though the enemy was only a few miles away, the equestrian statue of King George standing on Bowling Green was pulled from its pedestal and pounded to bits with hammers to be melted down into bullets for rebel guns.

On July 12, in an effort to test the rebel positions, General Howe sent a flotilla of ships up the North River. The forty-gun warship *Phoenix* and the twenty-eight-gun *Rose,* together with a schooner and two tenders, passed directly under the muzzles of Colonel Knox's shore batteries, firing broadsides into the town. Children ran for cover, women screamed and general pandemonium prevailed. Fascinated by the great spread of sails and the thunder of the guns, half of the Yankee artillerymen failed to report to their stations. Instead they ran along the riverbank, ogling the colorful flotilla as if it were putting on a demonstration on their behalf. The few gunners who did stand by their posts failed to register a single hit, and the ships continued on their way, practically unscathed, until they reached the safety of Tappan Zee, forty miles above New York. Colonel Knox was exasperated over the poor showing of his gunners. Washington was furious.

Six days later the flotilla came sailing back, this time under a heavy barrage of artillery fire. But by keeping close to the Jersey shore they managed to reach the bay and anchor without harm. The only casualties of the entire skirmish was a battery of Yankee gunners who were killed when their fieldpiece blew up in their faces. Inexperienced and overzealous, they had forgotten to swab out their cannon after each firing.

"It will serve as a lesson," said Colonel Knox, grimly. "And teach them to moderate their fiery courage."

Even at this time it was a well-known fact that General Howe and his brother Admiral Lord Howe were somewhat in sympathy with the rebel cause. On a number of occasions they had made strong public statements declaring their stand. It was for this reason, perhaps, that King George placed them in command of the forces sent to suppress the uprising and at the same time gave them wide powers for pardons and negotiations.

And so, before they went ahead with any attack or outright act of violence, Lord Howe sent an emissary of peace to talk with these wayward subjects. Henry Knox was a delegate to this meeting. He described it vividly in letters to his wife.

July 15, 1776

Lord Howe yesterday sent a flag of truce up to the city. They came within four miles of the city and were met by some of Colonel Tupper's people, who detained them until his Excellency's pleasure should be known. Accordingly, Colonel Reed and myself went down in the barge to receive the message. When we came to them, the officer, who was, I believe, captain of the "Eagle" man-of-war, rose up and bowed, keeping his hat off: "I have a letter from Lord Howe to Mr. Washington."

"Sir," says Colonel Reed, "we have no person in our army with that address."

"Sir," says the officer, "will you look at the address?" He took out of his pocket a letter which was thus addressed:

"George Washington, Esq., New York"
"Howe."

"No, sir," says Colonel Reed. "I cannot receive that letter."

"I am very sorry," says the officer, "and so will be Lord Howe, that any error in the superscription should prevent the letter being received by General Washington."

"Why, sir," says Colonel Reed, "I must obey orders."

"Oh, yes, sir, you must obey orders, to be sure."

Then, after giving him a letter from Colonel Campbell to General Howe, and some other letters from prisoners to their friends, we stood off, having saluted and bowed to each other. After we had got a little way, the officer put about his barge and stood for us and asked by what particular title he chose to be addressed.

Colonel Reed said, "You are sensible, sir, of the rank of General Washington in our army?"

"Yes, sir, we are. I am sure my Lord Howe will lament exceedingly this affair, as the letter is quite of a civil nature, and not a military one. He laments exceedingly that he was not here a little sooner"; which we suppose to allude to the Declaration of Independence; upon which we bowed and parted in the most genteel terms imaginable.

July 22, 1776

On Saturday I wrote you we had a captil flag of truce, no less than the adjutant-general of General Howe's army. He had an interview with General Washington at our house. The purpose of his message was, in very elegant, polite strains, to endeavour to persuade General Washington to receive a letter directed to George Washington, Esq., etc., etc. In the course of his talk every other word was, "May it please your Excellency." "If your Excellency so pleases"; in short no person could pay more respect than the said adjutant-general, whose name is Colonel Paterson, a person we do not know. He said the "etc., etc." implied everything. "It does so," said the General, "and anything." He said Lord and General Howe lamented exceedingly that any errors in the direction should interrupt that frequent intercourse between the two armies which might be necessary in the course of the service. That Lord Howe had come out with great powers. The General said he had heard that Lord Howe had come out with very great powers to pardon, but he had come to the wrong place; the Americans had not offended, therefore they needed no pardon. This confused him.

After a considerable deal of talk about the good dis-position of Lord and General Howe, he asked, "Has your Excellency no particular commands with which you would please to honour me to Lord and General Howe?"

"Nothing, sir, but my particular compliments to both"—a good answer.

General Washington was very handsomely dressed and made a most elegant appearance. Colonel Paterson appeared awe-struck, as if he was before something supernatural. Indeed I don't wonder at it. He was be-fore a very great man indeed. We had a cold collation provided, in which I lamented most exceedingly the absence of my Lucy. The General's servants did it tol-erably well, though Mr. Adjutant-general disappointed us. As it grew late, he even excused himself from drink-ing one glass of wine. He said Lord Howe and General Howe would wait for him, as they were to dine on board the "Eagle" man-of-war; he took his leave and went off.

As the fruitless negotiations dragged on, the British strength increased as more and more transports jammed the harbors in and around Staten Island. Squinting through his telescope, Henry Knox could see the regi-ments of English Grenadiers and Hessian mercenaries dis-embarking from the waiting transports. He could see the hundreds of fieldpieces being hoisted over the sides into the waiting lighters and the tons of supplies and ammuni-tion. Before long Staten Island became an armed camp, choked with mountains of ordnance and materials, billet-ing an army of thirty-two thousand professionally trained, battle tested soldiers, backed by a navy second to none. It was the largest expeditionary force ever assembled by the British Empire.

All of this was soon to be arrayed against an amateur army of farmers and shopkeepers, badly trained, poorly equipped, untested and completely inexperienced. It was the struggle of a David against a Goliath.

With the big attack expected almost any day, Henry Knox worked from sunup to sundown strengthening his positions, scraping together every piece of artillery he could find, setting them up along the defenses of Brooklyn Heights, Long Island and the approaches to Manhattan. He wrote to Lucy asking her about the baby and keeping her up to date on the impending invasion.

And in the meantime he waited. Along with General Washington and the rest of the little patriot army, he waited for the inevitable blow to fall. It came on August 22, 1776. The British landed on Long Island, and the battle for New York began.

6

HENRY KNOX WAS NOT THERE when the British landed on Long Island. He did not see the hundreds of longboats sliding in on the sands of Gravesend Bay, discharging their battalions of Redcoats and Hessians. He could hear the angry thunder of the distant guns, but he could not see the chaos and disorder that followed as Howe sent a strong flanking force around the American's left, encircling the small patriot army, hurling it back in wild confusion.

Waiting impatiently in his Manhattan headquarters, commanding his corps of artillery, he learned the shocking news of the defeat as it came in day by day. From messages and intelligence reports, from citizens and drifters, he heard about the savage battle, how thousands of frightened militia had thrown away their weapons, fleeing for their lives, enabling the enemy to sweep behind the lines. He heard too how Generals Sullivan and Stirling, along with hundreds of their men, had fought desperately to get out of the trap only to be outnumbered and captured by the Hessians. He was told about the gallant stand of the Delaware and Maryland regiments as three times they hurled back British attacks on the right, saving the patriot army from complete annihilation. He listened proudly to the many stories of his own artillery companies and how they stood by their guns, firing until the barrels were red hot, then moving on to new positions, continuing the fight all the way back to Brooklyn Heights.

He listened to all these things and he fretted and fumed, itching to be in the battle, helping to stem the British tide. But he was a good soldier, and his orders were to stand fast and remain at his post to cover a possible naval attack against New York.

As the anxious days passed, news of the disastrous defeat became more ominous. The Americans were hemmed in now along a five-mile front of Brooklyn Heights, their backs to the river, a wide mile of water between them and salvation. If the British frigates could sail up that stream and blast the American lines from the rear, the war would be over. The fight for freedom would flicker and be snuffed out like a sputtering candle.

But the weather was in the patriots' favor. The wind was from the northeast and the British men-of-war held fast to their anchors, unable to risk the shifting tides.

On the afternoon of September 19, when things looked blackest, Henry Knox was ordered to report to his Commander-in-Chief. He found Washington standing in front of a farmhouse surrounded by members of his staff. They had just come out of an urgent meeting and were deliberating over last-minute details. Darkness was settling over the Brooklyn farmlands, and in the dim light Knox could make out the familiar figures of Generals Putnam, Spencer and Mifflin and others. He could see the dark hollows under Washington's eyes, and his heart ached at the sight, knowing the suffering and humiliation of the tall, proud man.

The Virginian put his hand on Knox's arm and drew him aside, his voice low, unsteady with fatigue. "We're going to evacuate," he said. "It's the only thing left. We've got to save what we can, and we've only got a few hours of darkness to do it. That's why I called you over, Henry. I want you to take charge of the landings down here. McDougall will handle the one above."

Henry was shocked. They were going to evacuate. It was preposterous, utterly impossible. For three long months they had been building up troop strength here on Long Island. An entire regiment had been ferried across the day before, and now there were probably ten thousand men in the lines, as well as all the artillery, ammunition and equipment. How were they ever going to get all that out in one night with the enemy only a few hundred yards away? It was utterly impossible. He stood there thinking of all this, looking at this tired, weary man; but he said nothing.

"It's important," Washington continued, "important that the men don't know what's going on. I want to avoid any chance of panic or confusion. Just tell them they are being relieved, that other units are taking over their positions. Colonel Glover's and Hutchinson's units will man the boats. We'll start as soon as it's dark."

The boats came in quietly, with muffled oars, scraping their bows softly against the wharf. In long columns, regiments and companies marched down to the landing place, speaking in undertones, waiting patiently to fill the boats. Then Knox gave the orders—not in his big, bull-like voice but in a quiet hush of a whisper, muffled by the silken handkerchief twined about his disfigured hand.

"All right, men, move along. First brigade, Pennsylvania, boat number one. Easy now, no crowding, plenty of room for all. Here, soldier, take this along with you."

He handed the man an extra musket that he had found discarded in the bushes. "We might need this another time. Off you go now, keep the noise down, no talking."

He watched as the heavily laden craft disappeared into the darkness, caught up in the swirling current. As fast as the empty boats came in, he ordered them filled and started them on their way.

The enemy was only six hundred yards away, digging approaches to the American lines, completely oblivious of the hasty withdrawal. One mistake, one suspicious sound, and they would come swarming down on the retreating army like a horde of angry hornets.

Hour after hour the winding columns continued their movement down to the river, men from New York and Massachusetts, from Connecticut and Virginia, tired, dirty and utterly exhausted, men who had faced a living hell of fire and steel for almost a week, now waiting to take their place in line, waiting for a chance to rest, to eat and to live without the sound of exploding shells or whining bullets ringing in their ears.

Then Knox's own artillery companies came down, dragging their fieldpieces with them, loading eight- and nine-pounders, charred and broken ramrods, ammunition and equipment onto the boats. Some of the heavier guns sank up to their hubs in the soft marsh grass. The men pushed and shoved to get them free. The few that were hopelessly mired were left where they stood, and Henry groaned inwardly at the sight of his precious mortars and howitzers sinking in the slimy ooze.

Still they came on, the long lines of men, horses and equipment. At one point, a cannon that had hurriedly been pulled out of the lines went off by mistake. The ear-splitting boom reverberated through the silent night.

Knox scowled and held his breath. If the enemy were alerted now, the entire operation would be in jeopardy. But as the minutes passed and nothing happened, the retreat continued without mishap.

All night long Henry Knox paced up and down the riverbank supervising the loading, directing the evacuation. The fishermen from Marblehead and Salem worked tirelessly sailing the sloops and barges back and forth across the river. They manned dinghies, fishing smacks, yawls, scows, whaleboats—anything at all that was capable of hauling a cargo of men and supplies.

As morning came, the danger grew. There were still hundreds of men left in the lines, rear-guard units under General Mifflin, brave men who had stayed behind to cover the retreat of the others. With daylight coming the British would soon discover the ruse and the thinly held positions would be overwhelmed by a flood of angry Redcoats. But now, miraculously, just as the first light of dawn washed across the eastern sky, a thick, pea-soup fog rolled in like a benevolent curtain of mist. The final units were pulled from the lines and loaded into the boats.

Henry Knox was among the last to leave. As he sat in the boat with his Commander-in-Chief and pulled out into the fog, he could hear the British grenadiers charging the empty trenches and firing a ragged volley after the fleeing boats. He sat in the stern, his cloak wrapped tightly against the dampness. He was cold, tired and exhausted, and his head sank against his chest in fitful sleep. Somehow the incredible, impossible task had been done.

In less than twelve hours almost ten thousand men and their equipment and baggage had been evacuated across a mile of water under the very nose of the enemy. It was one of the most spectacular maneuvers in the history of warfare. It was not a victory; it was a defeat. But in spite of all that, it was a tremendous accomplishment, and it saved remnants of the little patriot army to fight another day.

No drums beat out a lively tattoo, no fifes played a victory tune as the ragged, dispirited regiments made their way through the streets of New York. Instead the weary men shuffled through the alleys and back streets of the city in dark, angry moods. The little army that had gone out with such high hopes of victory came back beaten and ashamed. Everywhere the smell of defeat was in the air. Discipline and order were forgotten. Stragglers roamed the streets looting and plundering like wild beasts. Desertion became rampant. The amateur soldiers, the shopkeepers and farmers, with their muskets and rifles, found that war was no game. They had had their first taste of battle, their first sting of defeat. They wanted no more.

Desperately Washington tried to control his scattered forces. Looters were severely punished, deserters were court-martialed and officers were ordered to restore law and order. The entire army was reorganized to give it greater flexibility of command.

Washington now realized that although he had saved his men from annihilation, he had not yet saved them from the enemy. With unopposed sea power the British could land at any point on Manhattan Island and completely cut off the patriot army. To checkmate this possibility, he moved his main force into defensive positions above Harlem Heights. Entrenchments were also manned at scattered points along the river, with an additional force of about five thousand men under General Putnam stationed on the southern tip of the island to defend the city. Colonel Henry Knox, with a detachment of artillery, was a part of this group. It was an uncertain arrangement at best, but Washington hoped that in the event of an attack the thinly scattered troops along the river front could hold the line long enough for Putnam to retreat up the island to safety. A few days later, Congress granted permission to abandon the city.

But the word came too late. The big enemy warships were already storming up and down the river pounding the rebel positions in preparation for the landings. Then the barges and flatboats came in, unloading their regiments of Redcoats and Hessians. At the sight of the long lines of brightly uniformed troops advancing up the slopes, bayonets flashing in the sun, the frightened patriot militia again broke and fled in wild confusion. Fleeing for their lives, throwing away weapons and equipment, they ran blindly in all directions. Within a matter of minutes the entire defensive line had melted away, leaving the troops at the southern tip of the island exposed and vulnerable. Many of the officers tried desperately to halt the wild disorder. Washington himself rode among the panic-stricken men, shouting at them and lashing out with his riding crop, but to no avail.

Five miles to the south Henry Knox was just starting out of New York, leading his artillery companies up the Boston Post Road to Harlem. The long line of cannons and howitzers were pulled by slow-moving teams of oxen and draft horses. Baggage trains and supply wagons brought up the rear. Reluctantly Knox had to abandon his big twenty-four- and thirty-two-pounders overlooking the Battery. They were too ponderous to be taken along.

Now, all about him, Henry Knox could see other units passing him by, heading north in a mad rush to avoid being cut off. Calmly he continued his steady, crawling pace, inwardly rejecting the thought of another retreat. As he plodded along he could hear the thundering boom of the British guns and the ominous sounds of battle growing closer. Then, a mile further on, he came to a long ridge and saw General Silliman with his Connecticut regiments drawn up in battle array. Knox took one look at the rolling terrain. He remembered all the things he had read in the military manuals and the faint trace of a smile crossed his boyish face. He approached Silliman, who was now standing resolutely on the crest of the hill. "You're going to make a stand?"

Silliman was a thick, heavyset man with tight lips and a dark scowl. "Yes, damn it. I'm tired of running."

Knox grinned. "You'll need artillery."

Silliman nodded, looking at the line of fieldpieces drawn up on the road. "You're welcome, but you don't have to stay."

"I'm tired of running too," said the bookseller. He started shouting orders, placing his guns in position along the front, sending a few down into the gully to cover the flanks.

For an hour they waited in the blazing sun, listening to the thunder of the British guns, but they never saw the enemy. Then, from the north, they heard the sound of pounding hooves. All eyes turned and fingers tightened on the triggers. A moment later a rider came into view, and Knox recognized Major Aaron Burr, General Putnam's aide-de-camp. His horse was sweat-soaked and winded.

"They're sending help," said Knox. "Good, tell them to hurry."

The young major tried to catch his breath. "Not help,"

he gasped. "You have orders to retreat. You are to follow me."

Knox scowled. "We have had enough of retreat," he shouted. "Here we stand. Let them come."

Burr shook his head insistently. "Within another hour you will be surrounded. The British are already crossing the island."

"Then we'll fight our way out," said Knox.

"No," said the Major. "This way you can save nothing, not even your lives. If you follow me there is still time."

Henry Knox looked at Silliman. The man had suddenly shrunk within himself. His shoulders sagged, and he shook his head sadly. "All right, Major," he said, "lead the way."

Knox gave orders for the guns to be hitched up, but Major Burr protested. "There is no time. We must leave now if we are to escape."

Knox looked up in disbelief. "Abandon the guns?"

Burr was growing impatient. "Yes, the guns, the supply train, the ammunition, everything. Leave it, do you understand?"

Silliman glanced sheepishly at Knox, knowing how he must have felt. "Come, Henry, the boy is right. Leave them where they are."

Slowly the long line of disheartened men moved up the road. For a long moment Henry Knox hesitated, glancing back at the shiny brass fieldpieces standing defiantly in place. Then, with a heavy heart, he turned to catch up with the retreating column.

All afternoon they stumbled along under the hot, blistering sun, tramping through fields and woodlands, climbing over ridges and knolls, sometimes only a half a mile from the advancing British columns. It grew dark and began to rain, a steady persistent drizzle, as the weary, disgruntled men trudged the last few miles to the safety of the American lines.

Henry Knox was the last one in and Washington welcomed him with a sigh of relief, for rumors had come through that the young artilleryman had been killed or captured. But Henry Knox was not dead. He was tired, he was wet and he was angry; but he was still very much alive.

7

BY THE AUTUMN OF 1776, the little Continental Army had reached the utmost depth of despair. In five major engagements it had been battered, overwhelmed and beaten. Forced out of Harlem Heights, it had made a gallant stand at White Plains, only to be hurled back, taking a humiliating defeat at Fort Washington. Escaping across the Hudson, it hurried on, pursued by the enemy, and gave up Fort Lee without firing a shot. Now it was retreating across the face of New Jersey with the main body of the British Army hard on its heels. The outlook, the prospect for the cause of liberty, was grim indeed.

Through the sodden, rain-soaked countryside, Colonel Henry Knox rode with the retreating column. He rode beside his Commander-in-Chief while a cold, drizzling rain seeped through his tattered, faded uniform, soaking him to the skin. He saw the roadside strewn with muskets, bayonets, knapsacks and other trappings of war, discarded by the fleeing army. An angry frown crossed his face as he saw the countless pieces of field artillery, gun carriages and ammunition wagons abandoned along the side of the road, left to rust in the thick, red mud of the water-filled ditches. Then he felt an uncontrollable surge of frustration as he thought of all the other guns he had left behind at Long Island, New York and Fort Washington.

The Commander-in-Chief must have sensed his anger. "It's all right, Henry, we'll get more. There just aren't enough horses to haul them."

Knox tried a weak smile. "If only we could have held on at Fort Lee."

Washington shook his head. "It doesn't matter now, Henry."

"No," said Knox, "we've had bad luck, beastly luck, with circumstances against us all the way. But that won't last forever. Someday we'll be able to take the field and stand up to them man for man."

"Maybe," said the General. "But right now we've got to run, and we've got to keep on running even if we have to go into the mountains and fight from there."

They rode on in silence for a while, listening to the sloshing of the horses' hooves and the creak of wet saddle leather. Then Washington spoke once more. "But I'll tell you one thing, Henry, we'll never quit, we'll never give up."

Henry Knox straightened in the saddle. He felt better now. This was the kind of talk he liked. The knot of frustration in his stomach disappeared, and he began to smile.

And so they ran. They ran through New Bridge and Hackensack. They crossed the Passaic River at Aquackonock Landing and hurried on through Newark and Elizabethtown just as the enemy were coming in the other side. And as they ran the little army melted away, dwindled to a mere shadow of its former self. Enlistments expired, and the men deserted by the thousands. The paymaster went broke, entire regiments disappeared.

Trudging along with the retreating army was a stoop-shouldered, disheveled little man. At night he squatted around the campfire scribbling on tattered sheets of soiled paper, using the head of a drum for a desk. "These are the times that try men's souls," he wrote. "The summer soldier and the sunshine patriot will, in this crisis, shrink from the service of their country; but he that stands it now deserves the love and thanks of man and woman. Tyranny, like hell, is not easily conquered; yet we have this consolation with us, that the harder the conflict the more glorious the triumph." He was as ragged and threadbare as the army he traveled with. But he was its conscience, its inspiration and its guide. He was Thomas Paine.

And so, once again, the little army became an untidy, miserable rabble in arms—without shoes, without clothing, without arms or shelter. Wretchedly it staggered along, a slow-moving column of tired, weary men, plodding through the mud and freezing cold of early December.

Knox wrote to his brother William. "My constant fatigue and application to duty has been such that I have not had my clothes off for more than forty days. The Hessians captured our baggage during the retreat from New York and I lost most of my wardrobe. Perhaps you could obtain a few lengths of brown or blue cloth for me so that I may have new uniforms made."

To Lucy he wrote, "The army is in dire need of men with great ideas, men who know and understand military principles. General Washington is so bogged down in administrative detail that I often wish for some relief for him that he may give more attention to military matters."

It began to snow now. Blinding, wind-swept flurries swirled about the men, slowing their progress. The enemy followed in close pursuit. When they reached Trenton, Washington ferried his army across the Delaware into Pennsylvania, taking with him every boat, every barge, every raft for seventy miles up and down the river. Without means of transportation the British were unable to follow. There were no boats, there were no bridges. All they could do was stand on the Jersey shore and watch the last boatloads of rebels paddle away to safety.

But General Howe was content. He had chased the fox to its lair. Come spring he would smoke him out. As far as the British were concerned, the war was over. The officers wrote back to England saying that they had swept all before them. They would surely be home by summer. General Howe was so confident that he moved his entire staff, together with a large part of his army, back to the warm hearth fires of New York City, leaving a scattered string of fortified strong points from Princeton and Trenton all the way up to Amboy and Elizabethtown. He firmly believed that the fires of rebellion had finally burned themselves out. All that remained was to extinguish the dying embers—and the cold bitter winter might even do that for him.

But although General Howe correctly gauged the miserable condition of the patriot army, he completely miscalculated its mood. Like a savage beast, harried from cover to cover, it was growing angry—and that anger would soon make it turn and lash out with renewed vigor.

Once again the bedraggled American puppy-dog was getting ready to nip the heels of the British lion.

The man who was to play a major role in making this all possible was a fugitive Tory spy from Giggstown, New Jersey. For more than a week now, John Honeyman had been working in and around Trenton, procuring supplies, meat and fowl for the British forces. On this morning of December 22, 1776, he was walking down the River Road, presumably looking for more cattle to bring in for slaughter. He was a short, heavyset man of Scotch-Irish descent, with close-cropped reddish hair and a ruddy complexion. Ostensibly he was working as a butcher and horsetrader, but he was well known for miles around as the "Tory Trader," a man who blatantly despised the rebel cause and openly supported the enemy.

Shuffling along with his peculiar bowlegged gait, he carried a whip and a length of rope, implements of his trade. He glanced from left to right, searching the fields for cattle, pigs or fowl that might be offered for sale. He had not gone far when he spotted a mounted rebel patrol coming down the road. For a moment he hesitated. Then he noticed a thin, spavined cow feeding on the dry forage in a nearby field. It was not the kind of animal he was likely to buy, but if his ruse worked he would be in luck. Quickly he stepped into the field, looped the rope about the cow's neck and began pulling her toward the road. He was almost there when he felt the cold muzzle of a pistol pressing against the nape of his neck.

"Hold it right where you are, Tory!"

John Honeyman turned and looked up into the black barrel of the weapon as the mounted man leveled it at his head.

"Where do you think you're going?"

"I'm a butcher," said Honeyman. "I'm taking this cow to slaughter."

The rebel laughed roughly. "For the British of course."

"Aye, for the British."

The soldier looked down at him with contempt. "All right, corporal, tie him up."

The second man dismounted and grabbed for Honeyman's arm, but the butcher turned quickly, striking him across the side of the face with the whip. He started to run, but he had only gone a short distance when the heel of a spurred boot jammed into the small of his back, knocking him to the ground.

The mounted rebel stood over him, the cocked pistol pointing at his head. "I've a good mind to put a ball between your eyes, Tory. But I think you have information, and for that we want you alive."

They pulled him to his feet and tied his hands behind his back with his own rope. Honeyman's face was livid with rage. "Rebel scum," he cursed, spitting in the dirt. "They'll hang the lot of you before this is over."

The horseman laughed, tugging sharply on the rope. "Come along," he said. "We'll see who'll do the hanging."

They ferried him across the Delaware to Washington's headquarters, where they turned him over to the guards. "Found him down the road, three miles outside of Trenton. Says he's a butcher."

The guards eyed him coldly. "Butcher, eh. Tory dog is more like it, and a spy at that."

General Washington looked up as they brought him in. He scowled and looked the Tory straight in the eye, then dismissed the guards. "Wait outside," he ordered. "I want to question this man alone. If he tries to escape, shoot him on sight."

The Commander-in-Chief went over to the window and drew the blinds. When he turned around there was a smile on his lips. He walked up to the prisoner and put a big hand on the man's shoulder. "John, it's good to see you. I've been waiting for you. How did it go?"

The man grinned, his brown eyes open and friendly now. "Not bad, sir. But they're a bit rough with the ropes."

"Here, let's take them off." Quickly Washington untied the bindings.

Honeyman brought his hands from behind his back and began rubbing his wrists to restore the circulation.

"Sit down and rest," said Washington, drawing up a chair. "You look as though you could do with a mug of flip."

While Washington prepared the drink, Honeyman said, "They tell me things are bad."

"They are, John, worse than they've ever been. We're short on clothing, supplies, equipment—everything. Enlistments are up for most of the men. They're tired and discouraged. In another few weeks they'll probably go back to their homes, and I can't do a thing to stop them."

"What about Lee's troops?"

"They're here now. Sullivan brought them in after Lee was captured. And we have the Pennsylvania men now. But morale is bad. We've got to do something to restore confidence. We've got to have a victory."

"You could take one of their outposts," said Honeyman. "Princeton, Maidenhead, Trenton—none of them are overmanned."

Washington nodded. "Yes, we've been thinking about

that." He handed the man a steaming cup of flip. "What can you tell us that will help?"

Honeyman took a couple of swallows of the hot drink, then hitched himself around in the chair. "Until a few days ago there was a great deal of moving about, shifting of troops and that sort of thing. Now everything has pretty much settled down. Bordentown is held by three battalions of Hessians, together with a contingent of the British 42nd Highlanders. Princeton, as you probably know, is under the command of General Leslie, with about twelve hundred men. They have another outpost at Maidenhead, a few miles down the road."

Washington sat at the writing table, jotting it all down with a quill. He let Honeyman finish his report; then he asked, "And what about Trenton?"

John Honeyman looked up now, his eyes sparkling with new interest. "Colonel Johann Rall is in command there. He has his own Hessian grenadiers, and the von Lössberg fusiliers and another regiment under Knyphausen. They are supported by about twenty British horsemen, all members of the Queen's Light Dragoons, 16th Regiment. Their company of artillery consists of six three-pounders, usually stationed one behind the other in the middle of King Street—that is, when they are not being pulled about on parade. Colonel Rall dearly loves a show, complete with drums, music and artillery."

Washington smiled. "And what does he think of us?"

"He honestly believes that five hundred of his Hessians could annihilate the entire rebel army if only the Americans would come out and fight." Honeyman hesitated, then continued: "And he has one undying ambition."

"What is that?"

Honeyman grinned. "To capture you alive."

Washington's hand went up to his mouth to stifle a chuckle. "Perhaps he'll soon get his chance," he said. "How many men do you estimate Colonel Rall has?"

"About fourteen or fifteen hundred, counting the pickets and yagers."

Washington was silent for a moment, then he spoke. "So their wings are spread," he said quietly. "Perhaps now is the time to clip them off."

Honeyman put down his empty cup and got to his feet.

"You've done an excellent job, John. What you've told me is worth a regiment. It's certain to save lives and bring our moment of victory closer. But now I'm going to ask you to do one more thing."

The man turned, waiting for the unexpected order.

"Go back to Trenton and report to Colonel Rall."

Honeyman winced.

"I know it's risky, but if they had any reason to doubt you they'd hardly expect you back. Besides I want you to tell them how weak we are, how impossible it would be for us to attack."

"That would kind of put the lid on the pot, wouldn't it?" said Honeyman grinning.

Washington nodded.

"You'll get in touch with my family, sir?"

"I've already done that, John. I sent your wife a letter explaining your position, and I've given orders that she is not to be molested in any way."

"Thank you, sir. I appreciate that. It's just that it's difficult to risk your neck for your country and be hated for it at the same time."

"For that, John, we all owe you a debt of gratitude that we can never repay."

They walked to the door, and Honeyman put his hands

behind his back while Washington tied them with the rope. "One more thing," said the General. "As soon as you've reported to Rall, I want you to get out of Trenton."

A glint of understanding shone in Honeyman's eyes. "Perhaps I'd better. It wouldn't do to get caught in the middle."

Washington smiled. "Good luck, John." Then he flung open the door and the expression on his face returned to its dark scowl. "Guard," he shouted. "Take this man away and keep him under arrest. He is to be court-martialed in the morning."

During the night a mysterious fire broke out in the prisoner stockade. The guards left to help put it out. When they returned, the door to the jail cell was open and John Honeyman was gone.

Darkness was just settling over the Pennsylvania countryside as Colonel Henry Knox cantered down the road to Newton. He turned in at the Samuel Merrick house, where the council of war was to be held. When he reached the cobblestone courtyard he gave his horse to an attendant, saluted the sentry at the door and entered the long, rough-hewn dining room.

General Washington was already there, with Generals Greene, St. Clair, Mercer, de Fermoy and Stephen. Generals Stirling and Sullivan, both of whom had been captured at Long Island and later exchanged, were also there, with other members of Washington's staff. After the Reverend Alexander McWhorter of Newark said grace and asked the Lord's blessing on their dangerous mission, they sat down to a dinner prepared by Mrs. Merrick.

When the meal was over and the dishes cleared away, the Merrick family discreetly left the room and the meeting began. The Commander-in-Chief motioned to his aide, Colonel Baylor, who spread out a large map of the surrounding area, showing the network of roads leading into and out of the enemy positions.

Washington glanced about the room, waiting for the murmur of voices to subside. "Gentlemen," he said, "tomorrow night we will cross the river in force and attack the enemy post at Trenton." The assembled staff nodded in approval. "According to our latest information," he continued, "the town is held by three regiments of Hessians and a small contingent of British light horse. The total force is estimated at about fifteen hundred men."

"General Ewing will take his men across just south of Trenton and seize the bridges over Assunpink Creek, cutting off the main line of retreat. General Cadwalader will cross near Bristol and create a diversion at Mount Holly and Bordentown. In the meantime I will lead the main force of two thousand, five hundred men in a direct assault on Trenton. We will begin ferrying operations early tomorrow night in preparation for a dawn attack."

Washington's glance went around the room, stopping at Henry Knox. "What do we have in the way of artillery, Henry?"

"Eighteen guns, sir, six-, four- and three-pounders and two howitzers, all ready to go."

"Do you anticipate any trouble?"

"No, sir, I've checked the Durham boats for width and draft, and the gun carriages will fit nicely."

"Good," said Washington. "Take your full eighteen then. We'll be needing them."

He turned to tall, taciturn Colonel Glover. "How does the river look, John?"

The rugged Marblehead marine stood up. "The river's clear all the way up to Burlington, sir. The current is swift on the off-shore approach, but I'm sure my men can manage the boats without too much trouble."

Washington nodded. "Then we all know what we have to do. Instruct your units to cook up four days' rations and caution your men to keep the utmost silence on the approach to the town. Good discipline and good march order can make the difference between success or failure."

The General folded up the map, and the chairs scraped across the floor when the men stood up. As the officers filed out of the room into the chilly night, Washington put his hand on Henry Knox's shoulder. "Henry, I'll need a good strong voice out there on that beach tomorrow night."

Knox's grin spread from ear to ear. "You can count on it, sir. I'll bellow like a bull."

When John Honeyman broke out of prison he fled through the fields and woods, traveling by night, and made his way back to Trenton, where he reported directly to Colonel Rall.

"They're finished," said Honeyman. "Their men are deserting by the thousands. They're down to three thousand now, and most of those are sick and unfit for duty."

Colonel Rall grinned. "Ya, dis ist vot I tink. Der ist no danger of attack." He smiled down at Honeyman. "You do goot yob. You get captured, you get information, you escape."

Honeyman winked at the Hessian commander. "Yankee dumkopfs," he said.

The colonel threw back his head in laughter, slapping

the horsetrader on the back. "Now you go get beef and applejack for my grenadiers, ya? Tomorrow ist Christmas. Ve haff big celebration."

8

CHRISTMAS DAY dawned cold, gray and damp. Early in the afternoon it began to snow, just as the American regiments were assembling in the sheltered valley behind McKonkey's Ferry. Twenty-five hundred men gathered under the dull, overcast sky, stamping their feet in the freezing mud, swinging their arms to keep warm, waiting for the order to march. Each of them carried a blanket, a knapsack with four days' cooked rations and forty rounds of ammunition. Many were poorly clad, wearing only summer clothes without coats. Some were actually barefoot, while others had strips of cloth wrapped about their feet in place of shoes.

For the first time in over a year they were going to attack, they were going on the offensive. To a defeated, demoralized army it was a heady prospect. It was a reckless, madcap venture, but it was gallant—better than running away.

Across the Delaware, in the little village of Trenton, the Hessians were celebrating Christmas. There were music and games, singing and drinking, all to the sound of hearty German laughter. The Commander of the garrison, Colonel Johann Gottlieb Rall, gave little thought to the rebel army. It was only a mob of ignorant yokels anyway, farmers and shopkeepers who ran for their lives at the first sign of a flashing bayonet. He haughtily dismissed all reports of the impending attack as idle chatter. In spite of innumerable warnings from his superiors, he stubbornly refused to dig entrenchments, set up roadblocks or strengthen his position in any way. Instead he frittered away the time inspecting his personal guard and conducting frequent dress parades up and down the village streets. On Christmas day he entered actively into the festivities, drinking with his officers and later paying holiday visits to wealthy Tories of the neighborhood.

Toward evening the wind blew up in strong northeast gusts, the temperature continued to drop and the snow came down in driving, windswept flurries. Under cover of darkness the patriot army marched from its assembly area to the landing place at McKonkey's Ferry, on the Pennsylvania shore of the Delaware. The men moved down quietly, shielding their faces against the biting wind, waiting their turn to board the boats.

For the past week, units of the New Jersey militia had been roaming up and down the river, commandeering barges, rowboats, gondolas or any other type of craft that could be used to transport men and equipment across the river. They were now brought down from their hiding places in the swamps and backwaters to the waiting troops. Most useful of all were the big Durham boats, shallow draft vessels forty to sixty feet long, specially constructed to carry iron ore from Durham Furnace to Philadelphia. Pointed at both ends, with an eight-foot beam, they were ideally suited for the task of hauling men and artillery.

At the point of embarkation the Delaware River was a

thousand feet across. The day before, as Colonel Glover had reported, it was a placid, smooth-flowing stream. That night it was a raging, ice-choked torrent, its far shore hidden in a blinding curtain of snow.

General Washington sat astride his chestnut sorrel mare, his cloak wrapped tightly around his shoulders, and supervised the operation. Twenty yards away, Colonel Henry Knox paced the riverbank, his huge 240-pound bulk silhouetted against the white background of snow and ice. With head thrown back and hands cupped around his mouth he relayed the orders of his Commander-in-Chief in powerful, stentorian tones.

"First Virginia Continentals, board your boats. Step lively, lads, advance party first, Connecticut regiments follow." His great bull-like voice carried out over the howling winds and the crashing sounds of the swirling ice floes, echoing against the distant shore. As soon as the boats were filled he ordered them off. "Steersmen, man your sweeps."

At the command from Knox the big boats pushed off, their keels scraping on the sandy bottom. The boatmen jammed their poles into the shallow river bottom and began walking aft along the running boards, pushing the boats ahead of them while steersmen held the tillers fast, guiding the boats upstream against the sweeping current.

Cracked and broken by the violent storm, the river ice surged downstream from the backwaters and tributaries. In huge jagged cakes it crashed against the sides of the boats, blocking their way and throwing them off course. It took all the ability, all the mastery of these Marble-head mariners to keep the loaded boats on an even keel. These were the men of Glover's regiment, the same men who had helped save the little patriot army on the retreat from Long Island. Now they showed the same deep-water skill, the same dogged perseverance they had portrayed on that fateful day six months ago. It was cold, backbreaking work, shoving aside the heavy ice and steering between the floes; but the men were determined, and the big Durham boats continued their steady progress back and forth across the river. Dinghies, rowboats and smaller craft brought in supplies and ammunition.

Back on the Pennsylvania shore Henry Knox continued his battle with the elements, bellowing out a steady stream of orders and commands, keeping the long lines of regiments and companies filing into the boats.

"New Hampshire brigades, move along there. Fill the boats on the left. Keep it moving. Pennsylvania troops next. Easy, lads, stand by those horses."

The Pennsylvania Troop of Light Horse led their animals up the improvised ramps, coaxing them along. The skittish horses reared and whinnied, frightened by the unstable footing, the slippery decks. Men shouted, holding fast to halter leads, maneuvering the animals into place.

The bitter wind cut through the tattered clothing of the ill-clad men. Fingers cramped, feet froze, faces and ears grew numb. Yet the traffic of men and equipment continued, in spite of the freezing cold, in spite of the snow, in spite of everything.

As soon as the initial units were across, Washington turned his horse over to an attendant and boarded one of the waiting boats. Henry Knox climbed in beside his Commander-in-Chief and sat down on the edge of the starboard beam. As soon as the boat was filled, it shoved off into the swirling current. A glum, depressing silence hung over the little party as they fought their way through the drifting ice. It was snowing harder than ever, and the freezing cold winds seemed to dampen the spirits of officers and men alike.

Halfway across, Washington glanced down and noticed the loaded boat tilting at an acute angle to starboard. A flicker of a smile crossed his lips, and in a gruff voice he said, "Shift your weight, Henry, before you sink the boat."

For a brief moment the droll words seemed to hang on the frosty night air. Then, as Henry Knox moved cautiously to the center of the boat, the men around him began to guffaw. Their booming laughter rang out in the darkness, and the joke was shouted across the water from one boat to another. Henry, too, was doubled up with laughter, his huge frame shaking with mirth, the tears running down his fat cheeks. He experienced a mixed feeling of pride and buffoonery. It was the kind of joke he dearly loved, and it gave him a close sense of comradeship with his Commander-in-Chief. As soon as they reached the opposite shore the amusing story was passed from man to man. It lightened their spirits and served to take the edge off the tense period of waiting.

Once they were on the Jersey shore the cold, arduous operations continued. Washington sat on an old beehive, directing the landings. Henry Knox paced the riverbank like a modern-day beachmaster, relaying his commander's orders.

Hour after hour the units continued to stream ashore. Finally the ponderous fieldpieces and the artillery horses were ferried across and brought up onto the road. It was three o'clock in the morning before the last boatload reached the Jersey shore, almost four hours behind schedule. Those precious hours could make the difference between victory and defeat. If the element of surprise were lost, if the enemy were alerted, he would be in a position to turn and drive the little patriot army back across the river, cutting it to pieces as it tried to navigate the ice-choked stream. There would be no recovery from such a defeat. But it was a chance they had to take. They had staked their gamble, and they had to go on. There was no turning back.

Even now, as they began the long march down the road towards Trenton, a Bucks County farmer borrowed a horse and galloped ahead of them to warn the enemy of the impending attack. Breathlessly he ran through the streets of Trenton, searching for the commanding officer. Minutes later he found Colonel Rall at the home of a wealthy Tory, celebrating Christmas. The servant refused to let him in, so the man hastly scribbled a note on a scrap of paper. "The rebels are marching on Trenton." When Rall received the message, he heedlessly stuffed it into his pocket, unread. It was the thoughtless behavior of a self-centered, overconfident man, an unwitting act that was soon to change the course of history.

In the meantime, the half-frozen, ill-clad throng that was the American army stumbled and shuffled its way down the road to Trenton, nine miles away. Henry Knox rode along with a contingent of his artillery, listening to the steady *clop, clop* of the horses' hooves on the rough, icy road. The wheels of the big gun carriages bounced and rattled over the frozen ruts, the trace chains clanking dully in the cold night air.

The snow had turned into a stinging, windswept sleet, coating the men with ice, crusting in their hair. Here and there Henry saw a man stumble and go down, then pick himself up and stagger on. It was a torturous, agonizing

ordeal, with each step a painful effort of will. Still the men
went on. None faltered, none gave up. The password was
"Victory or death," and the ragged band of patriots
marched on with this one thought in mind.

Many of them wrapped sacking about their muskets to
protect the primers against the dampness; but as they
marched along, the word began to filter down the line—
the flints were wet, priming powder had turned to a grimy
paste, the guns would not fire.

Washington received the news calmly. "Tell the men
to fix their bayonets," he replied grimly. "I am resolved
to take Trenton."

Years later Henry Knox would remember this night.
He would remember the bitter cold that knifed through
his shabby uniform like a thousand steel blades. He would
remember the deep, hacking coughs of the men as they
plodded along, heads down, shielding their faces against
the howling gale. He would remember the gray, silent
farmhouses, with the sleet beating against the darkened
windows, and the eery stillness as they passed through the
moving shadows of the hickory stands and black oak
forests. He would remember the misty white cloud of
vapor that hung over the panting column and the thousands of trampled footprints in the snow, many of them
tinged with blood. All these things he would remember,
but for now he thought only of his guns, because with
wet flints and useless muskets he knew this was going to
be a battle of artillery.

At the village of Birmingham, almost halfway to Trenton, the column stopped for a brief rest and a quick bite.
Minutes later they were ordered to form up again. Many
of the men were sprawled in the snow, fast asleep. Two

of them could not be aroused at all. They had frozen to death where they lay.

From Birmingham the column split in two, General Sullivan leading one of the sections down the River Road to come in from the south. Washington led the other along the Pennington Road to converge at the upper end of town.

With the first light of dawn both columns reached the outskirts of Trenton. The surprised Hessian pickets shouted the alarm, but it was too late. The rushing patriot battalions surged over and around them like a wave of vengeance. The surprise was utter and complete.

Within minutes the Americans had virtually surrounded the town. Cannons were brought up at a gallop, unlimbered, rolled into position and fired down the main streets. Henry Knox was everywhere at once, directing his artillery, dashing from battery to battery, shouting his orders above the din of battle.

"Battery one and two, round shot, battery six, grape. Charge your pieces, prime and fire." The six-pounders roared, shattering the dawn with their thunder, belching forth fire and shot. Cannoneers pulled them back into position at the end of drag-ropes, swabbed out the smoking barrels and rammed home another load of ball and shot. "Charge your pieces, prime and fire." Once again the guns thundered, amid a boiling cloud of acrid smoke.

Hessian troops tumbled out into the streets, trying to form up for volleys in a desperate effort to stem the tide. But it was no use. The Americans were already taking the barns and houses, drying out their flints, firing from windows and rooftops.

Through the snow and the sleet the battle continued, across Front Street, up and down King and Queen Streets and along Assunpink Creek. Colonel Rall was out of his quarters now, groggy and unsteady. Mounted on his horse he galloped about, trying to rally his men. But the patriots quickly broke up the Hessian formations, pressing the attack from every quarter.

Colonel Knox's artillery bore the brunt of the battle, fighting from street to street, his officers and men behaving like heroes. Captain William Washington and his lieutenant, James Monroe, the future president of the United States, saw the Hessians rolling a gun into position on King Street. Before the enemy could fire they rushed the position and captured the gun, although both were slightly wounded in the action. Captain Thomas Forrest and Captain Alexander Hamilton, each with a battery apiece, cleared King and Queen Streets, driving the enemy back into an orchard on the outskirts of town.

Twice Colonel Rall tried to rally his men for a counterattack. He charged about, frustrated and enraged. It was unthinkable that a motley band of farmers could outfight his veteran regiment of Hessians. In a fit of blind anger he galloped down the street shouting, "All my brave grenadiers, form up and follow me." But he had only gone a few feet when a musket ball struck him in the side and he fell from his horse mortally wounded.

The Americans were swarming through the town now. General Sullivan's men, coming in from the south, cut off the enemy's main line of retreat. A few escaped by swimming Assunpink Creek and making off towards Princeton. The rest were hemmed in by the Americans, who were rapidly closing in on all sides. Completely surrounded, without a leader, the well-trained, highly vaunted Hessian troops raised their tall fronted hats on the points of bayonets, a compliant gesture of surrender.

Within less than an hour the battle was over. The little patriot army had redeemed its honor and won a complete and stunning victory.

Henry Knox was jubilant. It was a day to celebrate, a day of new hope, truly a day to remember. Almost a thousand prisoners were taken, together with six brass field-pieces, a number of supply wagons, forty horses, thousands of muskets and rifles and enough musical instruments to equip half a dozen regimental bands.

Forty kegs of rum and brandy were also captured. They would have been a welcome reward for the tired, thirsty men, but the situation was still precarious and an entire army was yet to be ferried back across the river. Because of this, Washington reluctantly gave the order to have the spirits dumped. Silently, with long faces, the details went about their work, smashing the kegs and watching the liquid contents flow away down the streets.

The victory at Trenton shocked the British high command and caused a flurry of panic. General Cornwallis, who was about to leave for England, was called back to take command of the British forces in New Jersey. All posts along the Delaware were evacuated and the troops pulled back to less vulnerable positions. The rabble of farmers and shopkeepers were proving to be an unpredictable and stubborn foe.

9

A FEW DAYS after the battle of Trenton, Henry Knox wrote to Lucy: "It will give you great pleasure to know that Congress has appointed me to the rank of brigadier general in command of the artillery. It was unsolicited on my part, though I cannot say unexpected. I am afraid people are more lavish in their praise of my endeavors than I deserve. I wish only to serve my country with every effort in my power. My only regret is that it keeps me away from you." He went on to tell her about their great victory at Trenton, concluding: "War, my dear Lucy, is not a humane trade and the man who follows it, as such, will meet his proper demerits in another world."

Henry Knox was a brave and capable soldier, but he did not like war. He could fight with courage and bravery when it was necessary to defend his country or his liberty; but, like most good soldiers, he often wished there were another way.

In spite of the stunning victory, in spite of high morale, the little patriot army continued to dwindle and fade away. The men had fought courageously and well. They had served their country willingly while thousands of others had merely stood by and done nothing. Now their time was up, and understandably they wanted to go home. But now, more than ever, they were needed. The fledgling

American army had proved it could fight and that it could win. Now it had to prove it could survive.

Dressed in his buff-lined, dark-blue uniform with flashing epaulettes, General Henry Knox rode among his regiments, talking to the men, seeking to persuade them to stay, to re-enlist.

"Just a few more weeks, boys, that's all we ask. Just long enough for the new regiments to get here. We've got the enemy on the run. If we quit now we may never get another chance."

He looked at the blank, expressionless faces and he knew how they must have felt. They had been asked to do so much, so much more than their share, and there was still so much more to do. He could hardly blame them for wanting to leave, but at the same time he could not let them go.

Riding up and down the lines, he roared at them in his great bull voice. "We can stand up to them now, we know that. So let's finish the job. Congress has voted a ten-dollar bonus for every man who stays." He waited a moment for the offer of good hard cash to sink in. "Who'll give a few more weeks to our glorious country, six more weeks for victory?"

Here and there a man glanced at his companion and nodded. Together they stepped out of line and volunteered. Others followed suit, and soon entire regiments were offering to stay.

All over camp the story was the same. General Washington and General Mifflin were bringing in hundreds of men, urging them to re-enlist, calling on them to help save their country. Once again the tired, weary, underfed patriots responded, staying to save the ragged army from disaster, to fight another day.

That day was not long in coming. Stung and enraged by their surprise defeat at Trenton, the British sent a powerful force of regulars under General Cornwallis to avenge the insult. Eight thousand strong, they stormed down the road leading to Trenton and caught the little American army between the Delaware River and the sea. By the evening of January 2, 1777, they were within striking distance, ready to close the trap. This time Cornwallis was sure there would be no escape.

But Washington was still the master of maneuver and evasion. Under cover of darkness he took his army on a wide swing around the British left, over a rough and little-known road, to come up behind the enemy and attack their outpost at Princeton. It was another long, arduous march in bitter cold weather over icy roads, under the worst possible conditions. Cannons bogged down, and horses slipped and fell; the weary, overtired men stumbled along half asleep.

To mislead the British and cover up the secret withdrawal, four hundred men remained behind, throwing logs and brush on burning campfires, digging entrenchments and in general keeping up the appearance of a fully occupied camp.

At dawn the following day, the British advanced and found nothing but empty trenches and the dying embers of hundreds of campfires. Yet twelve miles to the rear they could hear the booming thunder of guns and the sounds of battle. While the British were attacking a deserted camp the Americans were taking Princeton.

But Princeton was not like Trenton. This time there was no surprise. Just as the exhausted patriot army reached the outskirts of town, they met a strong force of British regulars coming in the opposite direction. Once again Knox's artillery went into action, firing in close support of the American columns, breaking up the British formations.

At one point, a battalion of enemy infantry took refuge in Nassau Hall on the campus of Princeton University. They barricaded themselves in, blocking the doors, firing from the windows. When they refused an offer of surrender, Knox ordered a brass four-pounder into position. Young Captain Alexander Hamilton commanded the gun. His first shot flew through a window and smashed an oil painting of King George hanging on the wall. His second struck a cornice of the building, shaking it to its foundations. When the smoke cleared, two hundred British infantrymen came streaming out with their hands in the air.

The battle lasted less than thirty minutes, ending in a complete victory for the Americans, although they paid a heavy price. General Mercer, Colonel Haslet, Captain John Fleming and scores of other brave officers and men were lost.

Sixteen miles away, in the little village of New Brunswick, was a British war-chest filled with seventy thousand pounds of silver, a welcome addition to the dwindling patriot coffers. But to get it would mean another forced march, more fighting and the risk of being encircled. It was a tempting prize, but Washington took stock of the bitter, freezing weather and the exhausted men and decided that the need for rest and reorganization was more urgent. After a hasty council of war he gave orders to march north to Morris Plains, there to set up winter quarters, replenish supplies and recuperate.

In a rage of blind fury the British stormed down the road toward Princeton, hoping to intercept the Americans before they got away. To hold them back, small detachments of infantry and engineers were sent out to fight a delaying action, blowing up bridges, felling trees and setting up roadblocks. As they came up the Post Road the British were stopped by the threatening menace of six huge cannons mounted above them on overlooking ridges. Frustrated and impatient, Cornwallis deployed his men in a flanking maneuver to surround the guns and put them out of action. The move took up valuable time as the men climbed the heights and then rushed the guns from either side. They found they had been duped again. The big cannons were nothing more than useless hulks of broken artillery, left there by Henry Knox to delay the enemy advance. The ruse served its purpose, and by the time the British reached Princeton the Americans were well on their way to winter quarters and safety.

Flanked by mountains on one side and swamps on the other, the broad plains outside of Morristown made an ideal defensive position for the weary patriots. With the exception of New Brunswick and Amboy, most of New Jersey was now clear of the enemy, and the American army could settle down to an uninterrupted period of rest and recovery.

General Knox made a hurried trip to New England to speed up the enlistment of new recruits and make arrangements for the procurement of supplies and clothing. At Springfield, Massachusetts, he established an arsenal for the casting of cannons and the manufacture of guns and ammunition. During his errand he stopped off to see Lucy and his daughter, but his visit was all too brief. A few days later he was on his way back to Morristown.

William Knox and Lucy were still making efforts to re-establish the Boston book store, and it was about this time that William wrote to Henry telling him about a purchase of quills, paper and sealing wax. "The cost is two hundred pounds," he wrote, "and I think I shall make a pretty profit." Their inexperienced efforts were not always successful, however, and Henry continued to receive numerous letters of complaint concerning the difficulties of the business.

Lucy had given birth to her second child, a son. She wrote to Henry frequently, asking permission to come to Morristown with the children. But Henry had no wish for a repetition of the close call that had occurred at New York. As long as Lucy remained in Massachusetts she would be safe. He wanted her to stay there, where he knew his little family would be comfortable and secure.

In her next letter Lucy told Henry of a rumor that her brother was with the British forces in New York. "I devoutedly hope it is not true," she said. "But if it is, I shall write to him and tell him to come home. It is such a horrid war. It has taken you away from me, and now it may even cause you to draw your sword against my own brother."

This was the only news Lucy had heard about her family since the evacuation of Boston over a year ago. For Henry, a man of compassion and fraternity, this was hard to understand. "Even though your parents are on opposite sides," he wrote, "it is strange that it should divest them of all humanity. Not a line? My God, what stuff is the human heart made of?" Henry went on to tell her that although her entire family might desert her, he would always consider her his dearest treasure of Heaven.

As the war went on, scores of foreign officers were coming to America to take part in this new fight for liberty. Many of them were sincere and conscientious, like the Marquis de Lafayette, Count Casimir Pulaski and

General Duportail. But others were little more than professional opportunists grasping at a chance for quick fame and fortune.

It was on this subject that a warning now came from Lucy, taking Henry by complete surprise and throwing the little camp into dismay and confusion. Lucy wrote, "A French General du Coudray, who styles himself commander-in-chief of the Continental Artillery, is now in Boston. He says his appointment is from Mr. Dean and that he is going immediately to headquarters to take over command. Who knows but I may have my Henry back again? Of this I am sure, he will never suffer anyone to command him in this department. If he does, he does not have the soul that I now think him possessed of."

General Philippe Charles du Coudray arrived in Morristown with an imposing entourage of eighteen staff officers and ten sergeants, all ready to take over immediate command of the American artillery. The United States Commissioner in France, Silas Dean, soliciting help for the American cause, had officially made the appointment, and du Coudray had the papers to prove it.

Knox's fellow officers were incensed; General Washington was furious. Letters of protest flew back and forth between the American high command and the Continental Congress at Philadelphia. Washington wrote a personal letter to John Hancock, president of the Congress, stating that General Knox was a highly respected and valuable officer, possessed of unusually sound judgment and ability. He went on to say that General Knox had, in spite of innumerable difficulties, placed the artillery on a footing that did him the greatest honor. A change in command at that time, Washington said, would put the whole artillery in a state of confusion and chaos.

Knox threatened to resign if Congress gave the command to du Coudray, although, in a letter to Lucy, he wrote: "I am determined to contribute my mite to the defense of my country, in spite of every obstacle." Generals Sullivan and Greene sent a stinging message to Congress, rebuking that body for even thinking of such a move, and for a few days the situation was tense and unpleasant.

The problem was finally solved when Congress appointed du Coudray Inspector General of Ordnance and Military Manufacturies. A few weeks later, du Coudray was drowned when he and his horse fell overboard from a barge while crossing the Schuylkill River.

For six months the patriot army remained at Morristown, reorganizing and gaining strength. Along with the steady stream of officers the French sent an occasional boatload of badly needed weapons and supplies. The ranks, left vacant by desertions and overdue enlistments, were partially filled with new recruits from Pennsylvania and New England. The men were gradually clothed and re-equipped, and once again the patriot army was ready for the field.

On the Sunday morning of August 24, 1777, it marched through the city of Philadelphia. General Henry Knox rode at the head of the column beside his Commander-in-Chief and the Marquis de Lafayette. Eleven thousand strong, they made an impressive sight as they came down Front Street past crowds of cheering citizens. The Philadelphia Light Horse and the Virginia Dragoons rode by on their prancing steeds, flanked by rows of flashing bayonets with rumbling cannons and brass fieldpieces bringing up the rear. It took almost an entire day for the long column to pass through the capital city.

On September 11 the American and British forces clashed at Brandywine Creek. It was a savage, hard-fought battle over rough and difficult terrain, marked by individual courage and heroism. At many places the Americans fought in a magnificent delaying action, making the enemy pay dearly for every foot of ground. Knox's artillery served gallantly, standing by their guns, continuing to fire even when pressed and surrounded. All day long the battle raged back and forth, with flanking movements, feints and counterattacks. But by nightfall the enemy held the field and the Americans were falling back. Realizing that the day was lost, Washington moved north slowly before the advancing British. The Continental Congress fled to Lancaster, Pennsylvania, and the British occupied Philadelphia. But though it was a defeat, it was not a rout; though it was a retreat, it was not a panic. The American army was learning to fight and learning to retreat—but not to run away.

A month later the Americans tried again with a four-pronged attack against Germantown. At first all went well. The enemy was being pushed back on all sides, and victory seemed imminent. Then the American center was held up by a strongly fortified house standing directly in the main line of attack. It was a large stone structure known as the Crew House, defended by four companies of British regulars, firing from the second-story windows.

It was here that Knox made his first and only tactical blunder. At a hurried meeting of the staff Washington was advised to bypass the strong point and press on with the attack, but General Knox objected. Remembering the military treatises he had read as a boy, he cautioned against leaving an occupied castle in the rear. To prove his point he set up a ring of artillery and began pounding away at the obstinate stronghold. His light fieldpieces battered down the windows and doors but made little impression on the thick stone walls. To make matters worse, a heavy fog began to roll in, covering the entire area. In the resulting confusion the American troops became hopelessly disoriented, wandering about and firing on their own brigades. What started out as almost certain victory ended in stalemate and defeat. Although Knox's mistake helped to bog down the advance, the major cause of the failure was the changing weather and the thick rolling fog.

After months of marching and two major campaigns the American army was again spent and exhausted. Practically unclothed, its weapons worn and rusty, it faced another long winter of freezing weather, sickness and privation. Like a tired, wounded beast, it dragged itself along the winding roads of Pennsylvania, covering less than thirteen miles in one week, heading for a place on the Schuylkill River called Valley Forge. A lush green in summer, the valley was now a leafless, snow-covered expanse of earth without warmth or shelter.

Here the men built makeshift cabins of split logs chinked with sod, erected in scattered regimental rows. The huts were drafty and damp, and the men slept on the bare, earthen floor with only a thin covering of straw for a mattress. But far worse than the inadequate shelter was the almost complete lack of food and clothing. There was no fresh meat and only an occasional chunk of salt pork or strip of smoked herring. A daily staple was a gummy paste made of flour and water and baked on heated stones over a sooty fire. The men ate it for breakfast, dinner and supper. After years of campaigning, their uniforms were little more than tatters. Many of the men wore nothing but shabby blankets about their shoulders and strips of burlap wrapped around their feet. Medical attention was virtually nonexistent, and the undernourished troops came down by the thousands with typhus, smallpox, dysentery and frostbite. Vermin of every description infested their living quarters.

One of the major difficulties in obtaining provisions was the lack of transportation. Roads into the area were frequently blocked by snow. Supply wagons and carts caught out in the heavy storms were left stranded until the spring thaws would release them. Hundreds of draft horses and artillery mounts died for lack of fodder. Foraging parties continually seached the surrounding farms and villages, but after two years of war and occupation the countryside had little more to offer.

The British, meanwhile, were billeted snug and secure in Philadelphia, passing the winter in comparative comfort. Washington's scouts hung around the outskirts of the city, keeping the enemy under close watch. At Valley Forge, sentinels stood guard in the tops of the tallest trees, keeping a constant lookout for roving bands of enemy cavalry.

All too slowly the interminable winter months wore on and the wretched conditions worsened. Dire predictions were on every tongue. There was talk of mutiny and desertion. A few more weeks, a few more days, and the army would literally disintegrate.

10

DURING THE COURSE OF THE LONG WAR the history of the little patriot army was a story of unbelievable hardship and privation, a series of tragic episodes, each one more desperate than the other. Yet out of this suffering and despair a new spirit was emerging. An almost miraculous change was taking place. It came about slowly, kindled perhaps by the first spark of victory at Trenton. It reached its climax during the squalor and misery of Valley Forge.

It began with a kind of pathetic humor, prompted by a bond of mutual suffering, as when two ill-clad, barefoot men met shivering in the cold, in the middle of a chill December drizzle.

"Good morning, brother soldier, and how are you?"

"All wet, thank you; hope you are the same."

"And what have you for supper?"

"Why fire-cakes, of course."

"Ah, a most tempting morsel."

"Perhaps you would consent to dine with me?"

The first soldier bowed deeply. "How could I refuse such delectable fare?"

"Come, then, in your most elegant rags."

There was a new comradeship, a new sense of unity that had not been there before. It was evident in the rank and file as the men shared a handful of dried corn or a crust of black bread, as a tattered blanket was passed from hand to hand to warm a comrade standing guard, cover a sick friend or patch a worn jacket. It showed too as Pennsylvania troopers worked side by side with Connecticut militia under the command of a Rhode Island captain.

Although this new pride was instilled by mutual experience, it was surely nurtured and brought to fulfillment by an affable adventurer, an out-and-out impostor, who, in spite of his prevarications and pretensions, possessed the ability to turn an untrained rabble in arms into an efficient fighting machine.

He came to Valley Forge in the winter of 1778, and called himself Baron Friedrich Wilhelm von Steuben. His real name was Wilhelm Stube. He claimed to have been a lieutenant general in the service of Frederick the Great. He was in fact a retired captain of the Prussian Army. He spoke of a family estate in Swabi, Germany, when in truth he had no property at all. He was simply a soldier of fortune who had come to America to find a job and make use of his military talents. He had come to the right place and, fortunately for America, his talents were of a high caliber.

Henry Knox found him intelligent, witty and full of charm. Washington considered him the most able foreign officer next to the Marquis de Lafayette. Unlike most of his compatriots, von Steuben asked for no pay beyond his board and living expenses. He specifically requested that his rank be withheld until he had proved what he could do. Within two short weeks, Washington and his staff were convinced that von Steuben was worth the rank of major general, and he was so appointed.

Von Steuben found the army in a most deplorable condition—inefficient, undisciplined and without the slightest knowledge of drill or maneuver. Undaunted, he assumed the duties of a sergeant. With one hundred picked men, he began a rigid program of training and close-order drill. He spoke not a word of English, so he secured the services of young Captain Benjamin Walker of New York, who translated his commands. Von Steuben taught the men the basic movements of the platoon and company— slow step, half step and quick step, all the while shouting out the rhythm in a guttural Germanic cadence. By pantomime and sign language he showed them the rudiments of the manual of arms—how to load, to prime and to fire.

At first the men resented his brisk, swaggering style, looking upon him as little more than an arrogant Hessian impostor. But his charm, his wit and his evident ability soon won them over. At times he threw them into fits of laughter with his clownish antics; at other times he lost his temper, cursing them with every invective in his alien vocabulary. The men soon learned to know when he was joking and when he was serious and were quick to behave accordingly.

He established just rules of discipline and instituted regular periods of roll call in order that the effective fighting strength of the army might be ascertained at any given moment. The men came to respect and admire him, and thousands gathered around to watch as he drilled his elite platoons, learning as they observed. He could be stern and demanding, but he asked them to do nothing that he would not do himself. He arose at three o'clock each morning, and after a simple breakfast repaired to the drill field to begin his work, instructing by squads, by platoons and by companies.

When fully trained and proficient, each unit was sent
off to teach others. A new company would take its place
before the capable German drill-master. By late spring
the American army was still threadbare and ragged, but
now it stood straight and tall, its proud regiments aligned
shoulder to shoulder. Now it could maneuver and attack,
and it could execute a flanking movement as neatly and
efficiently as the most superbly trained British division
or Hessian brigade. The birth of the professional U.S.
Army may be marked by the date on which Baron Friedrich Wilhelm von Steuben first came to Valley Forge. He
may have been an impostor, he may have been a pre-
tender—but he was not a fraud.

With the coming of spring, conditions at Valley Forge
began to improve. Foragers were out, scouring over a wide
area of the Pennsylvania and Jersey countryside, driving
in herds of cattle and swine. General Nathanael Greene
was made quartermaster general, and soon the wagons
and carts began to roll, bringing in great loads of grain,
foodstuffs and supplies.

On a warm day in late March, sentries patrolling the
banks of the Schuylkill River noticed the waters foam-
ing and boiling in a most peculiar fashion. Closer inspection disclosed the reason for the commotion, and soon
the cry of "Fish, Fish" echoed on the balmy spring air.
From all over camp men rushed into the churning waters
with buckets, rakes, sacks and anything else that could
be used to scoop up the fat, silvery fish. It was the annual
spring migration of shad, fighting their way upriver to
the spawning grounds. Day after day the men harvested
the windfall of provisions, filling baskets, barrels and
wagons. Hundreds of thousands of the succulent fish were

baked, boiled or fried. They were made into chowder, fishcakes and patties, and literally tons of the fillet were salted down and put away for future use.

In a matter of days the men began to gain weight; their skin lost its gray pallor and took on a new ruddy complexion. They gained renewed strength, and the entire encampment perked up. From a place of squalor and disease, Valley Forge became an active, prosperous enterprise, filled with new life and new hope for the future.

A few months earlier, General Henry Knox and Colonel Paul Sergeant had been sent to New York to intercede with the convening legislature on behalf of the patriot army. They were to request shipments of food, supplies and uniforms and whatever else that governing body might be able to send. In spite of the lean conditions at Valley Forge, Henry Knox still managed to maintain a weight considerably in excess of two hundred pounds. His companion, Colonel Sergeant, was a dapper young man, dressed impeccably in a blue and buff uniform, complete with ruffles and braid. The two soldiers entered the meeting room with the dozen delegates and waited their turn to be heard.

After the preliminary speeches were over, Henry Knox got up and proceeded to outline the miserable conditions of the army. In pathetic terms, he described the lack of food, the disheveled condition of the uniforms and the acute suffering of the men. The delegates listened attentively, nodding their heads in understanding. When Knox had finished, the president of the assembly glanced about the hall and asked if there were any member who wished to make a comment.

One of the delegates, a tall, droll-looking gentleman,

got to his feet. He looked at General Knox, then at Colonel Sergeant, and smiled. "It may all very well be true," he said, "that our heroic army is in dire need of food and clothing. But if you will permit a rather pertinent observation, I have never seen a fatter general nor a better-dressed colonel."

The little assembly roared with laughter while Henry Knox held his ample sides, shaking with mirth. He could not talk.

The quick-thinking Colonel Sergeant saved the occasion. "You are quite right, sir," he replied. "But in deference to this legislature the army has seen fit to send its only member with a superfluous ounce of flesh and its only officer with a complete suit of clothes."

With the coming of spring and the flowering greenery at Valley Forge came the ladies to grace the headquarters and the mess tables. Martha Washington was already there, soon to be followed by Kitty Greene, the wife of General Greene, and Lady Stirling, the wife of General Stirling, and all the ladies and belles of the neighborhood. With all this conviviality and urbanity, Lucy Knox could hardly be left out. She swooped down on the camp like a mother hen and literally took over the social life of the community. It was a colorful gathering, considering the times, and the ladies frequently met at General Knox's headquarters to sew uniforms and leggings, to bake pies and bread and to make up baskets of food and medicine for the men.

Spring also brought other good tidings. France officially recognized the promising new country of the United States of America. Formal treaties were signed, and aid, in the form of supplies and men, was promised.

The day of May 17, 1778, was set aside to celebrate this event. There were speeches, parades and festivities. The regiments marched past the reviewing stand in splendid formation, showing off their best alignment and maneuvers. Accompanied by fifes and drums, the battalions and brigades turned and wheeled with perfect precision. Mounted on a sturdy horse, General Knox paraded his batteries of shiny artillery and later gave a thirteen-gun salute. Later that evening there was a gala reception with refreshments and a dance. As usual, stout, jovial Henry Knox and his equally portly wife were on hand to act as a reception committee, greeting the dignitaries and mingling with the guests.

To show appreciation for the French acceptance, Congress ordered all officers of the Continental Army to take an oath of allegiance to the United States. On May 30, 1778, at the Artillery park at Valley Forge, General Henry Knox administered the oath to Major General Benedict Arnold.

General Arnold, dressed in his finest uniform, his powdered wig impeccably in place, his chest bedecked with decorations and medals, approached the platform where Henry Knox stood. He placed his hand on the Bible and repeated the solemn words after Knox.

"I, Benedict Arnold, Major General, do acknowledge the United States of America to be free, independent and sovereign states and declare that the people thereof owe no allegiance to George the Third, King of Great Britain; and I renounce, refute and abjure my allegiance or obedience to him; and I do swear that I will, to the utmost of my power, support, maintain and defend the said United States against the said King George the Third, his heirs and successors, and will serve the said United States in the office of Major General, which I now hold, with fidelity, according to the best of my skill and understanding."

For six long months the British occupied the city of Philadelphia, hoping the Americans would foolishly attempt to retake it. Then, by a process of attrition, they could wear down the little patriot army and end the war. But Washington refused to take the bait. He sat snugly in his stronghold at Valley Forge, gaining strength and waiting for the proper moment to strike.

It came on June 18, 1778. Realizing that their strategy was unsuccessful, the British evacuated the city and started back for New York. This was the chance Washington had been waiting for. He immediately set his army in motion, marching across New Jersey, following closely on the heels of the enemy columns.

The long line of American troops that marched out of Valley Forge was a different army from the one that had staggered into that snow-swept valley in the winter of 1777. Twelve thousand strong, it was fully manned, well equipped and confident. Drums rolling and fifes playing, it stepped off down the road, banners flying high, bayonets glistening in the sun. Henry Knox's artillery rumbled along behind the brigades. As they marched along the men sang and joked, their spirits high. They were ready to meet the enemy with a new feeling of pride and defiance. Never again were they to know the panic of disorderly retreat or the shame of complete defeat.

Three days later the two forces clashed at a place called Monmouth Courthouse, near Freehold, New Jersey. Under a blazing hot sun, the battle raged back and forth throughout the day. Casualties were heavy, and men on both sides dropped from sheer exhaustion under the blis-

tering heat. It was one of the longest, closest-fought battles of the war, but by nightfall the British were giving
ground. Washington waited for morning to resume the
attack, but when the sun came up the enemy was gone.
Under cover of darkness they had broken off the engage-
ment and continued their flight to the safety of New York.

Describing the conflict in his famous *Military Journal
of The American Revolution,* Dr. James Thacher later
wrote: "In the hard-fought contest at Monmouth, no
officer was more distinguished than General Henry Knox.
In the front of the battle he was seen animating the soldiers and directing the thunder of their cannon. His skill
and bravery was so conspicuous that he received the particular approbation of the commander-in-chief, in general orders issued on the day succeeding the battle, in
which he says that 'the enemy have done us the honor to
acknowledge that no artillery could be better served than
ours.' "

The war dragged on through 1779 and on into 1780.
There was fighting in the north and in the south and
brutal clashes in the back country of Pennsylvania. There
had been stunning victories at Saratoga and Stoney Point,
but neither the Americans nor the British were any closer
to victory.

On the morning of September 25, 1780, Henry Knox
accompanied his Commander-in-Chief on an inspection
tour of West Point. The fort was disorganized and poorly
manned—but even more baffling was the fact that no
one seemed to know the whereabouts of its commander,
General Benedict Arnold. Puzzled and uncertain, Washington and his staff made their way across the Hudson to

a nearby residence, where General Arnold frequently stayed when off duty.

As they approached the house, Knox saw young Alexander Hamilton, a lieutenant colonel now, pacing up and down, overwrought and excited. Washington had barely reached the steps when Hamilton thrust a packet of letters into his hand. Quietly Washington stepped inside and opened the packet. As he began to read, Knox saw his face turn white. Washington's hands trembled. When he looked up, his eyes were filled with tears. "My God," he said, "Arnold has betrayed us. Whom can we trust now?"

Knox shook his head in disbelief. General Benedict Arnold, a trusted friend and compatriot, had sold out to the enemy. It was unthinkable, impossible. Yet the evidence was there, in Washington's hands—documents concerning troop strength, ordinance and detailed plans of West Point, all found on the person of a British courier caught within the American lines.

But though Henry Knox was shaken by this incredible news, he was more stunned when he heard the name of the British spy. It was none other than Major John André. Quickly his thoughts flew back to the shores of Lake George, four years before, when, on his trip to Ticonderoga, he had met a young British officer and prisoner of war. He remembered the enjoyable midnight discussion, the young man's amazing intellect and gracious manners. He remembered, too, André's parting words: "Let us hope that someday we may meet again under different circumstances." How much more different those circumstances could be can hardly be imagined.

On Friday afternoon, September 29, 1780, the sun streamed in through the narrow windows of the old Dutch church at Tappan, New York. General Henry Knox and fourteen other high-ranking officers sat at the long wooden table waiting to try Major John André, Adjutant General of the British Army, for the heinous crime of spying. General Nathanael Greene was the president of the board. The Marquis de Lafayette, Baron von Steuben and General John Glover were among the other members.

A solemn hush fell over the gathering as the young British officer was brought in and led up the aisle to face his accusers. He looked much as Henry had remembered him—thinner perhaps, but still handsome and well composed. Within the five days since his arrest, André had enchanted his captors. Guards and officers alike found it difficult to resist his wit, charm and winning personality. He was consistently cheerful and well mannered, without the slightest trace of intrigue or deceit. Colonel Alexander Hamilton, who saw much of him during his imprisonment, thought him one of the most talented and brilliant men he had ever met. Lafayette considered him a soldier and a gentleman of the first rank. Now he stood before the court, smiling graciously as he was confronted by his judges.

The trial was brief and to the point. André willingly narrated the story of his misadventures, without reservation or evasion. He told how he had come ashore from the English war-ship *Vulture* under cover of darkness to meet with General Benedict Arnold on a secret matter. He freely admitted that he had later, although against his better judgment, changed his British uniform for civilian clothes in order to escape detection; that Arnold had given him the plans and diagrams of the fort at West Point and signed a pass to permit him safe conduct back to the *Vulture,* anchored in the Hudson River. He described how he had finally been apprehended and searched by an

American patrol, who found the incriminating evidence hidden in his stocking.

The board listened attentively, hoping that the personable young man might offer some evidence that would mitigate his case and make it possible for them to convict him on a lesser charge. But André spoke with an almost naïve innocence. He told the truth simply and candidly, without offering a single statement in his own defense.

Toward the end of the trial, General Greene made a final effort to give André a chance to save himself. "Is it not true, Major André, that because of the nature of your mission, you believed you were coming ashore under a flag of truce?"

The court held its breath while André seemed to be carefully weighing his answer. Then he spoke, "No, sir, that is impossible. If I had come ashore under a flag of truce I would have been able to return by the same sanction."

Henry Knox groaned inwardly, and the entire court felt a deep sense of gloom and frustration. By this blunt denial, John André had just signed his own death warrant.

Quietly André was led away and the board proceeded to vote.

General Greene went down the line of judges, stopping before each man. "What say ye?"

The word "guilty" was muttered by each in turn.

When he came to Henry Knox, the big artilleryman hesitated, his hands trembling. It was the most difficult decision he had ever been called upon to make. By intent and purpose Major John André was not a spy. He was merely a messenger, a courier between the British Army and General Benedict Arnold, an unwitting pawn in an abortive attempt at conspiracy. Had he affirmed the fact that he had come ashore under a flag of truce, and had he not discarded his uniform, he would have been held only as a prisoner of war. But now, according to the exact letter of the law, he was a spy.

On the other hand, the real criminal, the despicable Benedict Arnold, had made good his escape. By now he was safe and secure behind enemy lines, with a fortune in gold as his reward. It was unfair, it was contrived, it was cruel—yet it had to be. Finally, almost choking over the words, Henry Knox stammered out, "I find the prisoner guilty as charged."

By a unanimous vote, Major André was convicted and sentenced to be hanged at five o'clock the following afternoon.

Letters and messages were rushed back and forth between British Headquarters and the American high command. Emissaries came to plead for André's release. Washington sent out secret agents to entreat with General Clinton, the British commander in New York, in a final effort to save André's life. If the British would turn over Benedict Arnold, Major André would go free. Everyone hoped and prayed, from the Commander-in-Chief to the men in the ranks. But the British refused to budge. They hated and despised Arnold as much as they loved and respected André, but they had made a pact and they would not go back on their word. The execution was postponed for another day and the hurried meetings and urgent communications continued, but to no avail.

Finally, on the morning of October 2, the troops were drawn up, the hangman was ready and André was led to the gallows. Dressed in his scarlet military uniform, trimmed with blue and with flashing gold buttons, he made a splendid sight as he walked along. With trim, powdered wig and shiny patent-leather boots he was a picture of young manhood and respectability. Lithesome, almost debonair, he walked between the rows of troops, a cheerful smile on his lips. He passed the long line of mounted officers, nodding graciously to each in turn. As he came to Henry Knox, he hesitated for the barest fraction of a second and a flicker of recognition passed between them.

Then John André continued his brief journey to the gallows. Bravely he climbed onto the open wagon that stood under the scaffold. With his own hands he adjusted the noose around his neck and tied the blindfold about his eyes. Then, with a smile still on his lips, he stood ready and waiting. When asked if he had anything further to say, he replied only, "Bear me witness to the fact that I die as a brave man."

There was a momentary hush, and Henry Knox bowed his head and closed his eyes while tears of shame and remorse rolled down his fat cheeks. Then he heard the crack of the hangman's whip and the rattle of the wagon wheels, and he knew that Major John André was no more.

It is an ironic twist of fate that John André died as a martyr for his own country and a hero to the country he fought against. His bones are interred with the great at Westminster Abbey in London, and he is honored with a headstone bearing a noble inscription at Tappan, New York, on the spot where he was hanged.

11

FOR SEVEN LONG, WEARY YEARS the war dragged on across the length and breadth of the thirteen colonies. From Massachusetts to Georgia, from Philadelphia to Charleston, there were skirmishes and campaigns, victories and defeats. But the greatest battle of all, for the American Army, was the continual fight against hunger and privation, the lack of supplies and the ever-present threat of dissolution.

In the summer of 1781, the little patriot army still faced that same specter of poverty, want and starvation, and once again Henry Knox made a tour of the New England states in an effort to obtain the urgently needed food and clothing, to raise funds and to speed up the enlistment of recruits.

Yet to many, like Knox himself, this low ebb of American strength was set off by a new feeling of hope and encouragement. The French were in the war now, not only with supplies and equipment but with men. An entire French army, under Lieutenant General de Rochambeau, was encamped at Newport, Rhode Island, and a strong French fleet, under Admiral François de Grasse, was on its way from the West Indies. With their help, Washington hoped to invade New York and drive the British out of that vital port.

Then, just before the stage was set, a new and more immediate opportunity presented itself in the south. An entire British army, led by Lord Cornwallis, had marched into Yorktown, on the shores of Chesapeake Bay, and began preparations to settle down for the winter.

With shrewd foresight, General de Rochambeau suggested that the French and Americans surround the city and that the French fleet blockade the harbor, thus placing the British forces in Yorktown under a state of siege. Washington was quick to grasp the significance of the situation and sent his army on a forced march toward the south.

Knox knew that this next campaign was going to depend largely on him. Like all sieges, it would be a battle of artillery, of mortars and cannons, of entrenchments and parallels. Properly staged and conducted, it could lead to a major victory and perhaps end the war. With this goal in mind, he set about his task with energy and enthusiasm. He rounded up every cannon, howitzer and mortar he could find. He improvised gun carriages and carts. He requisitioned the Board of War for more supplies and ammunition. He pestered the individual states for additional men and equipment. He begged, he stole, he borrowed to get the transportation, the stores and equipment he needed.

In late September, the allied armies reached Yorktown and began the preliminary work of digging in, throwing up breastworks and redoubts. The artillery came by water from Philadelphia and was unloaded at Trebell's Landing, on the James River. With an acute shortage of transport, Knox commandeered the officers' horses and baggage wagons to haul the big guns over the six miles of road to Yorktown. Yet, even with this, many of the heavy weapons had to be dragged over the sandy roads by squads of men hauling at the ends of ropes.

Henry's early studies of Vauban and Saxe came in good stead as he laid out his gun positions and batteries. With the help of General von Steuben, he outlined entrenchments and parallels and drew up plans for the sappers and miners. He worked tirelessly, supervising the placement of every gun, mortar and cannon.

During this time he had the company of his brother, William, who had come down from Massachusetts to witness this historic event. No doubt Henry proudly showed him the huge eighteen- and twenty-four-pounders and the thirteen-inch mortars already in place, waiting only for the order to fire. Lucy, too, was not far away, staying with Martha Washington at Mount Vernon while her husband was busy setting up and directing his precious artillery.

With the French forces strongly dug in on the left, the American Army ready on the right and a French fleet riding at anchor in Chesapeake Bay, the British were in a precarious position. Surrounded by a total force of twenty thousand men, they could neither retreat nor attack. Cornwallis' only chance was the hope that General Clinton would send a relief expedition down from New York, but even this would have to fight its way through a rapidly closing ring of men and ships.

Shortly before the siege began Henry Knox was invited to accompany his Commander-in-Chief to a high-level meeting aboard Admiral de Grasse's flagship the *Ville de Paris*. The sailors and soldiers were drawn up on the deck in ceremonial formation. The flags of both nations were flying from the masthead, and the ship's band struck up a martial air. Washington, dressed in a bright-blue and buff uniform, stepped forward to greet the admiral. In true French tradition de Grasse flung his arms about the big man, kissing him on both cheeks, at the same time remarking, for all to hear, *"Ah, mon petit Général."*

There was a momentary silence; then a booming laugh echoed out over the distinguished gathering. All eyes turned to the source of the distraction. It was Henry Knox, standing in the middle of the deck, holding his sides as he shook with laughter. The sight of the little admiral kissing the six-foot general and calling him *petit* was more than his sense of humor could stand. The assembled guests must have taken this as a sign of the new American *laissez faire,* for they too permitted themselves a brief chuckle as they filed below for the meeting.

By October 9, all preparations for the siege were completed, the first parallel was dug, the cannons were in position and the men, who had been laboring under the harassment of the enemy guns, were itching to fire back. Since the French had completed their work ahead of the Americans, Washington gave them permission to fire first. With a thundering roar the big French batteries opened up on the British ships anchored in the harbor.

In the meantime Washington made a last-minute inspection tour of the American positions. Accompanied by Henry Knox, he went from battery to battery, nodding his head in satisfaction as the portly artillery chief pointed out the well-placed weapons. Then Knox led the General to a huge twenty-four-pounder, standing in its parapet, all primed and ready to go. With a flourish Henry picked up a lighted torch and handed it to his Commander-in-Chief. Pleased with this singular honor, Washington stepped up to the big gun and put the blazing torch to the touch-hole. A tremendous blast shook the earth as the cannon belched forth a column of smoke and flame, sending the first American round into the city of Yorktown.

All over the battlefield the other batteries opened up, pouring in shot and shell on the beleaguered town. Day and night the deadly bombardment continued, destroying the outposts, the buildings and harbor facilities. During the day the earth trembled with the thunder of the guns, while the blazing fires and the pall of smoke boiled up into the sky like a devilish inferno.

At night, the spinning mortar shells arched through the darkness, their burning fuses leaving a crescent trail of fire in their wake. The big siege guns sent their heavy balls of iron skipping across the ground to crash head-long into the enemy battlements, while huge mortars, mounted on specially designed carriages, fired point-blank into the walls. Within a few days the city was in ruins, a shambles of leveled buildings, the streets filled with rubble and debris.

In the beginning the enemy answered round for round, but as the days passed and their ammunition ran low their return fire slackened off and then died out completely. Slowly, methodically, the city was razed, block by block, building by building, and the enemy was forced to take refuge in caves or caverns dug into the ground. Even the shipping in the harbor was completely obliterated as the burning vessels set fire to the wharfs and docks.

Under cover of this continual bombardment, the allies dug their second parallel, a zigzag trench complete with parapets and earthworks, running to within one hundred and ninety yards of the enemy positions. More cannons and mortars were brought up until, by October 15, nearly one hundred guns were pounding the crumbling British stronghold.

One afternoon Colonel Alexander Hamilton came up to the parapet where Henry Knox was installing another of his big mortars. During the course of their conversation Hamilton remarked about one of Washington's recent orders advising the men to give warning whenever they saw a shell coming over.

"It's downright unsoldierly," said Hamilton, who prided himself on his fearlessness and courage.

Knox looked at him coldly. "And I think it's downright sensible. What's the use of getting one's head shot off for nothing?"

Hamilton laughed. "You can't win a war by ducking every time a shell flies over."

"Maybe not," said Knox. "But you're not likely to lose it that way either. There's a time for courage and a time for discretion, and a good general knows the difference."

Hamilton shrugged while Knox went on with his work. Minutes later a large mortar shell landed a few feet away, its fuse hissing and sputtering in the dirt. Without thinking, both men dived for a nearby trench. Hamilton reached it first and pulled the bulky Knox in on top of him, thus shielding himself from the impending blast. After the explosion the two men got to their feet, neither of them hurt. Knox shook an indignant finger in the younger man's face. "Now what do you say about crying 'shell,' Mr. Hamilton?" Then, brushing himself off, he continued, "And I'll thank you not to make a breastworks of me again."

Angry and humiliated, Hamilton walked off without a word.

For nine horrible days and nights the devastating bombardment continued. By now the British were completely out of food and ammunition. Sickness and pestilence haunted the city, and the chance of rescue had long since passed. For Cornwallis, there was only one thing to do. On the morning of October 17, a drummer boy, dressed in the scarlet uniform of the British army, mounted the center parapet. With the bombs and shells flying all about him he took his post and began beating out his message. At first the din of the cannons and mortars drowned out the sound. But then, one by one, the big guns ceased their fire. Over the smoke and pall of battle could be heard the steady roll of the drum, a formal sign of surrender.

A few minutes later, a British officer walked out of the battered fortress carrying a flag of truce. He made straight for the American lines, where he was blindfolded and led to the rear. There his message was sent to the Commander-in-Chief. A few hours later, an agreement for surrender was arranged.

On the following afternoon, under the watchful eyes of the American forces, the entire British army under Lord Cornwallis marched out of its crumbling fortress. With their bands playing "The World Turned Upside Down," the British troops meekly stacked their arms and regimental banners in an open field and officially conceded defeat.

It was a tremendous victory and, as Henry Knox said later when he wrote to Lucy, "It was a glorious moment for America."

Over eight thousand prisoners were taken, together with two hundred and twenty-four cannons, howitzers and mortars, thousands of small arms and great amounts of military stores and equipment. News of the important event quickly swept throughout the land. There was wild rejoicing, and the churches were filled with the faithful, who offered prayers of hope and thanksgiving.

Henry Knox wrote to John Adams, "The consequences will be extremely beneficial. The remaining enemy will now be confined to Charleston and New York, where he will be forced to fight a defensive war for those two posts."

In his official report to Congress, General Washington gave Knox full credit for his outstanding contributions to the victory. "The resources of his genius supplied the deficit of means," said Washington. At the same time, he recommended Knox for promotion to major general.

When the news of the American victory reached England it came as a final staggering blow. The British people were tired of the war, tired of its drain on their economy, of its casualty lists and sacrifices. In spite of King George's stubborn refusal to quit, Parliament voted overwhelmingly to end the hostilities and make peace.

And so, as Henry Knox had hoped, the siege of Yorktown was the last great battle of the war. After seven years of suffering, seven years of misery and defeat, the war was finally over. By the determination of its soldiers, the courage and loyalty of its citizen army, America had finally won its independence. All that remained was to sign the treaty.

A few days later Lucy Knox gave birth to another child, her fourth, a son. The boy was christened Julian, and General Washington was his proud godfather.

With the war all but over, Henry Knox was appointed to the command of West Point and its outlying defenses at Dobbs Ferry and Stoney Point. Promoted to major general, he made his headquarters at Newburgh. There he lived with Lucy and the children in a huge stone house, complete with spacious living rooms, kitchens and a veranda. He had always been inclined to portliness, but now, with the strenuous activity of campaigning over and the return to abundant living, he gained enormously, reaching a weight of two hundred and eighty pounds. Yet his height and military bearing gave him the appearance of a trim and well-proportioned man. Lucy Knox was on the heavy side too, but her dark, flashing eyes and wholesome complexion made her a beauty in spite of her weight. Happy and fun-loving, they were a well-adjusted and attractive couple.

During his command of West Point, Knox's chief concern was the deplorable financial condition of the officers and men. They had not been paid for many months, and most of them were penniless and destitute. Now that the fighting was actually over, a desultory Congress balked at the thought of raising the funds necessary to pay them off.

As the weeks wore on, the situation became worse. The men were angry. The officers, righteously indignant, formed into militant groups, threatening to take action if their promised pay was not soon forthcoming.

Knox wrote endless letters to Congress, pleading their cause, begging the secretary to do something about it before it was too late. "The expectations of the army," he wrote, "from the drummer boy to the highest officer are keen for some pay and I shudder at the thought of their not receiving it. It appears to me highly unreasonable that America, who under heaven is indebted to the army for her very existence, should not make some compensation for the value of its services."

Still unable to get action, Henry began to receive letters from officers and men begging for help. From a soldier in Philadelphia, he read, "I am in great need of pay.

Both myself and my wife are now sick and I have received no pay for almost three years now which please your honor it is very hard for me to live in such circumstances."

The situation finally reached a climax when Knox came across a secret document urging all officers to desert in a body and retire to the furthest reaches of the wilderness, leaving the ungrateful country to its fate. Disturbed by this threatening news, Knox informed Washington and a mass meeting was held a few days later. Washington personally addressed the gathering. As he began to read his opening lines he hesitated, then stopped. Reaching into his breast pocket, he took out a pair of glasses. "Gentlemen," he said, "you must pardon me. I have grown gray in your service and now find myself growing blind." He went on appealing to their better judgment, asking them to use moderation and restraint, promising them full support and a just settlement of their debts. It was only after this near-mutiny that Congress acted, pledging to appropriate the money for the back pay.

On September 3, 1783, a formal peace treaty between America and England was signed in Paris, officially ending the war. On November 25 the British army evacuated New York. As the last enemy troop ship sailed out of the harbor, Henry Knox entered the city at the head of the American Army.

On December 4, General Washington held a meeting at Fraunces Tavern on the southern tip of Manhattan to bid farewell to his officers and staff. Henry Knox was there when the Commander-in-Chief entered the room.

He could see the years of strain and suffering lined on the big man's face, and he noticed the trembling hands as the General toyed with a morsel of food.

The room was silent. All present turned to their beloved Commander, waiting for him to speak. Quietly Washington filled his glass with wine and held it up, waiting for the others to do the same. Then, in a voice choked with emotion, he said, "With a heart full of love and gratitude, I now take leave of you. I most devoutly wish that your later days may be as prosperous and happy as your former ones have been glorious and honorable."

When the toast was finished, Washington looked up, a mist of tears clouding his blue eyes. "I cannot come to each of you," he said, "but I shall feel obliged if each of you will come and take me by the hand."

As senior ranking officer, Henry Knox stepped forward. For a long moment Washington gazed into his bright gray eyes, perhaps remembering the many times he had depended on this loyal artilleryman for help and advice. He no doubt remembered also how this one man, of all his officers, had never given him a moment's worry or concern, had never once questioned his command or authority, even when he himself was filled with doubts and uncertainty. Suddenly, impulsively, Washington threw his arms around the fat general, hugging him and kissing him on the cheek, a sign of gratitude and admiration.

Then each of the officers stepped up, in turn, and paid their respects, one and all brushing the tears from their eyes. After the last man had been received and embraced, Washington walked quietly out of the room. He made his way down between the ranks of honor guard directly to the wharf, where a barge was waiting to take him across the river, on the first leg of his journey home to Mount Vernon. Thousands of people lined the way, shouting and cheering. As the barge moved away, Washington turned once more and waved his hat in farewell. Then the oarsmen bent to their oars, and Henry Knox watched with a heavy heart as his Commander-in-Chief disappeared towards the distant shore. The war was over, the hard, weary struggle for independence was won and its leader was going home. A new era was about to begin.

12

WHEN THE LAST GUN WAS FIRED, the final prisoner exchanged and the British flag hauled down from American soil, peace had finally come. The United States, at long last, was a free and sovereign nation. But if Henry Knox looked forward to an uninterrupted period of peace and prosperity, his hopes were doomed to early frustration. The new nation would grow and eventually become strong and united, but not without its share of strife and conflict, its agony of bloodshed and despair.

The last British ship had no sooner left American shores than the thirteen states began bickering and fighting among themselves. The causes were many and varied, most of them petty, a few of them fraught with significance. Settlers living on the borderline of adjoining states fought over land boundaries and water rights. Duly elected delegates to the national Congress were lax about attending; some failed to show up at all. War debts went unpaid. Taxes were difficult to impose and almost impossible to collect. Unreasonable tariffs were set up, drastically limiting the flow of materials from one place to another. Each state printed its own currency, often refusing to accept the currency of its neighbor. Jealousy and suspicion were rampant, and some states even threatened to secede from the confederation and establish themselves as separate nations.

Men like Washington, Adams, Knox, Jefferson, Hamilton and others reasoned and conspired, pleaded and schemed to keep the infant nation from floundering on the rocks of greed and self-interest.

New York, Connecticut and New Jersey were at odds over money and goods. Farm produce flowed into New York from the two neighboring states; in exchange, money flowed out. To counteract this drain on its economy, New York placed a high tariff on firewood, vegetables, poultry and meats. In retaliation, New Jersey imposed a stiff tax on a New York harbor lighthouse located at Sandy Hook.

Further south, Maryland controlled the Potomac River, claiming jurisdiction on both shores along its entire length. Not to be outdone, Virginia attempted to levy a toll on all Maryland shipping coming into or out of Chesapeake Bay.

One of the most serious clashes of all took place in western Pennsylvania, where a large group of Connecticut colonists had settled in the Susquehanna Valley. There they built their log cabins and plowed their farms, claiming the land for their mother state of Connecticut. Pennsylvania bristled with indignation, and Congress appointed a five-man board to settle the dispute. The verdict ruled in favor of Pennsylvania, and the matter was considered closed. Then exaggerated rumors began to circulate, telling of insurrection and rebellion among the settlers. To quell this supposed uprising, Pennsylvania sent out a small party of militia, under a brutal and ruthless leader. The result was a senseless massacre of hundreds of innocent people.

The settlers were hunted down like wild animals and

shot without compassion, while the old men, women and children were driven into the wilderness and left to make their way back to Connecticut the best way they could.

This near-anarchy and lawlessness continued and soon grew worse. There was no central authority to make the laws and, even if there were, there was no legally constituted body strong enough to enforce them. Each group, each state, took matters into its own hands, without regard to truth or justice. The new nation was a nation in name only. In reality it was an unruly collection of feuding states, each seeking its own self-interest and aggrandizement.

The one agency that might have been called upon to protect and defend the innocent was the army, but this too had been neglected until it was little more than a token force of ill-equipped men.

Even before the war was over, the army had begun to dwindle. Unpaid and poorly clothed, the men went home to their farms and shops with only the muskets they carried in their hands and the threadbare shirts they wore on their backs. As his last official act, Washington appointed Henry Knox the new Commander-in-Chief of the Army. It was Knox's duty to demobilize the men as quickly as possible. In 1784 he reported to Congress that the standing army numbered less than seven hundred men. Even this number was later cut. There were twenty-five men at Fort Pitt, fifty-five at West Point. One sergeant and three privates comprised the entire garrison of Fort Randolph, and the same number manned the national arsenal at Springfield.

As a reward for their service, the discharged veterans were promised bounties of land. With an eye to the future, Knox suggested that these be located west of the Ohio

River. There the officers and men could build new lives on rich, fertile soil and at the same time help protect the country's western flank. "In a very few years they would make the finest settlement on the frontier and form a strong barrier against the Indians," said Knox.

As with so many other suggestions, his motion was duly received, filed and forgotten. History and future Indian uprisings were to prove the wisdom of his proposal.

To help preserve the fellowship and loyalties engendered during the Revolution, Knox organized a group known as the Society of The Cincinnati. This was an organization composed solely of allied officers, regardless of nationality, who had fought in the Continental Army during the Revolution. Named after Lucius Quintus Cincinnatus, a famous farmer-general of ancient Rome, its purpose was to perpetuate friendship, preserve the rights and liberties for which the men had fought and give help and aid to their descendants.

At first there was loud criticism by many citizens not eligible to belong. Men like Franklin, Jefferson and Adams feared that Knox and his fellow officers were unwittingly creating a military dictatorship. Others said the society was under the influence of a foreign government, seeking to undermine the stability of the United States.

Guided by this criticism, the members were careful to confine their work to humanitarian and nonpolitical issues. They raised money for the construction of historical monuments, endowed professorships at leading universities and helped the needy. The membership grew in size and distinction, including such names as Washington, Hamilton, Greene, von Steuben, Lafayette, Wayne, Kosz-ciusko, Monroe, Mifflin, John Paul Jones and hundreds of others. With this long list of illustrious members and continued good work, the society soon lost its stigma of militancy and became a renowned and honored fraternity in the social life of the new nation.

In spite of the conflicts and violence, the shaky confederation somehow managed to survive and even display a semblance of unity. The Government was slowly organizing posts and departments to administer such vital functions as finance, defense, and international relations. On March 8, 1785, Congress elected Henry Knox, Secretary of War, with an annual salary of two thousand, four hundred and fifty dollars. His department was to include three clerks and a messenger, with an allotted expenditure of one hundred and seventy dollars to pay for fuel, candles and stationery.

Although it was meagerly endowed, Knox's department was charged with enormous responsibility. The duties of the new War Department consisted of keeping the peace, subduing insurrections, dealing with the Indians, protecting the frontiers and supervising the distribution of bounty lands. To accomplish all this, Henry Knox was given a regiment of seven hundred men. With a coastline over fifteen hundred miles in length and a western border equally as long, there were hardly enough troops to maintain a corporal's guard at any one point. As for suppressing Indian attacks along the frontier or privateer raids on defenseless coastal cities, this was simply out of the question. But as always, Henry Knox went about his new task with optimism and resolution.

With the government offices situated in New York City, Knox took up residence in a house on Bowery Lane. There he settled down with Mrs. Knox and the children, Miss Lucy, Julia, Marcus and Henry, Jr. The household also included a number of housekeepers, two indentured servants and a groom to take care of the horses and look after the stables.

The family was sooned joined by William, Henry's younger brother, who had recently visited in London. While there, he met a young English girl. He fell deeply in love with her and planned to marry. Unfortunately the lady did not consent, and young William considered himself snubbed and rejected. He became moody and depressed. A friend of the family wrote from London, informing Henry that William was mentally disturbed, failing in health and spirit. The disquieting news caused Henry deep concern. He immediately sent for his brother and arranged to have him work as a clerk in the war office, hoping the change would help him to forget. Surrounded by his little family, Henry Knox was happy and content.

Although he was pleased with his domestic state, however, he was far from satisfied with the state of the union. The antifederalists were still fighting and scheming to obstruct the formation of an effective, unified government, while the states continued to guard their precious sovereignty against the slightest infringement to higher authority. And what was worse, under the present articles of confederation, Congress was relegated to the position of little more than a formal debating society, powerless to act, even in times of crisis.

Henry Knox knew, as did many of his compatriots, that if the new nation were going to survive, if it were going to become self-reliant and free from the restraint of petty differences within its ranks, then drastic changes would have to be made within the structure of its constitution. This called for a strong central government, free to legislate and act for the good of the majority, with peace-keeping powers capable of guaranteeing the safety of the individual and the nation. It called for an immediate reduction in interstate tariffs, a common monetary system and an equitable code of civil laws.

To Henry Knox all this was self-evident, for only in this way could peace and prosperity be achieved. This, of course, was federalism, and it was in direct contrast to the views of the antifederalists, who believed in a limited form of government, subject to the will of the individual states.

And so the confederation muddled along, each state setting up its own rules and regulations with total disregard for the others. The situation reached a climax in 1786, when Massachusetts imposed a heavy tax on its landowners. The small farmers in the central and western part of the state were hit hardest of all. Unable to raise the money to meet the unreasonable assessments, these men were being dispossessed by the hundreds, losing their land and their very livelihood. Hundreds more were thrown into debtors' prison. Many of them were veterans of the Revolution who, only a few years before, had fought to save their country from this very same kind of unjust taxation.

The situation was tense. Tempers reached the boiling point as mobs of irate farmers converged on the local courts, disrupting the sessions and abducting the judges in an attempt to halt further proceedings. A young officer of the Revolution, Captain Daniel Shays, began to organize the unruly mob. He mobilized them into an army of twelve thousand men, ready to fight and to overthrow the government if necessary.

Although many of the states had long been simmering with resentment over unfair taxes, the situation in Massa-

chusetts had all the portents of a civil war. Henry Knox
was shocked. As Secretary of War, he immediately advised the government to raise an army and quell the uprising before it got out of hand, but as usual Congress
was powerless to act.

Washington received the news with surprise and disbelief. "Good God," he exclaimed, "who besides a Tory
or a Briton could have predicted such a situation?"

In January of 1787, with no opposition in sight, Shays
and his men began marching on the government arsenal
at Springfield to confiscate the stores of weapons and
ammunition. Realizing that Shays meant business, Massachusetts mobilized a force of four thousand men under
the command of General Benjamin Lincoln.

But on January 25, Lincoln and his army were still
fifty miles away as Shays stormed down the snow-covered
Post Road to attack the arsenal. General Shepard, the
officer in command of the arsenal, was heavily reinforced,
with orders to protect the government property at all costs.
He waited till Shays's men came into sight, then sent out
an emissary, stating that if the insurgents moved any
closer, he was prepared to fire.

Shays's answer was a jeering laugh. With a wave of his
hand he gave the order to attack, and the entire force
swept forward.

Within the building, Shepard and his men aimed two
small fieldpieces over the heads of the advancing men.
The guns roared with a blinding flash of smoke and flame.
For a brief moment the rebels were stunned, then at a
word from Shays, they swarmed on again. Quickly Shepard gave the order to lower the guns. This time they fired
point-blank into the charging mass. When the smoke
cleared, three men lay dead in the snow and another was

badly wounded. The insurgents were shocked, and they milled about uncertain. Then, by tens and twenties, they turned and started running for the hills.

A few days later General Lincoln arrived with his militia and pursued the rebels through cold, freezing weather to the borders of Vermont. There they were rounded up and taken prisoner, except for Shays and a few others, who escaped over the border into Canada.

Knox complimented General Lincoln on his fine work. "You have dissipated a cloud that threatened to become a violent storm," he said. When the insurgents were brought in, he advocated leniency and hoped they would be treated with justice and tolerance. His feelings were shared by many who felt the farmers had a just cause for complaint. After swearing an oath of allegiance to the Massachusetts General Court, the insurgents were released and granted a full pardon. A few years later Shays returned to the United States and took up residence in the state of New York.

The need for a strong federal government to bring unity and order to the new nation was now clearly evident. If a small band of angry farmers could threaten the safety of an entire nation, then it was high time something was done about it.

"I do not conceive that we can exist long as a nation," said Washington, "without having lodged somewhere a power that will pervade the whole union in as energetic a manner as the authority of the state governments extends over the several states."

Even Thomas Jefferson, a staunch antifederalist, remarked, "I find the conviction growing strongly that nothing can preserve our confederacy unless the bond of union be strengthened."

The clamor for action was strong, and a national convention of the thirteen states was soon announced. It was to be held in Philadelphia in May, 1789, for the express purpose of outlining and implementing a new federal constitution.

As an official member of the government Henry Knox was not eligible to take part in the proceedings, but through letters and conversation he made his opinions known and did all he could to arouse support for a unified, effective government.

On the other hand, as a private citizen, Washington was free to attend. Yet he hesitated, because he feared the convention would produce little, if anything, of lasting value. This was not like the General, and Knox was deeply concerned. He wrote to his old Commander-in-Chief, impressing on him the need for national unity in the forthcoming assembly and the importance of his participation. "I take it for granted," he wrote, "that however reluctantly you may acquiesce, you will be constrained to accept the president's chair. And if an energetic and judicious system be proposed, with your signature, it would be a circumstance highly honorable to your fame and doubly entitle you to the glorious epithet—"the Father of Your Country."

On May 25, 1787, the convention finally got under way at the State House in Philadelphia. Twelve states sent a total of fifty-five delegates and, as Henry Knox had predicted, George Washington was elected to be the presiding officer. For four long months the delegates met behind closed doors, putting forth proposals and counterproposals, debating the pros and cons of local versus federal power, making compromises and concessions.

In June the temperatures climbed into the nineties.

Tempers grew short. Accusations were made and members threatened to quit. Yet somehow the delegates struggled on. When the final speeches were over and the convention opened its doors, they had hammered out one of the most remarkable and monumental documents in the history of man. It began: "We the People of the United States, in order to form a more perfect Union, establish Justice, insure domestic Tranquility, provide for the common Defense, promote the general Welfare, and secure the Blessings of Liberty to ourselves and our Posterity, do ordain and establish this Constitution for the United States of America."

Henry Knox was jubilant. The sorely needed power of the federal government had been secured. It was far more flexible, far more comprehensive than he had dared hope for.

Yet the new document had one final hurdle to pass before it became official. It had to be approved and ratified by at least nine of the individual states. Failing this, the four months' work of the convention would have been in vain.

Henry Knox got busy. He wrote letters to friends and acquaintances all over the country, to men of influence, men in local government and on the fringes of politics, expounding the merits and virtues of the new constitution, its fair and just regulations, its flexibility and provisions for adjustment. Wherever he went he spoke in glowing terms of the excellent government that would result under the guidance of this historic proclamation. It would bring prosperity and national solidarity. Always optimistic, he looked forward to the day when the country could take full advantage of its endless resources and opportunities. The new constitution, he felt, would stimulate just such endeavors.

Other men and other forces were also working hard for ratification. Correspondence with friends in Virginia, Connecticut, New York and New Jersey kept Knox in touch with the mood of the people. The general consensus seemed to be in favor of the new government, yet he knew the vote could be close. Hopefully he waited.

In December, 1787, Delaware was the first state to ratify, followed by Pennsylvania a few days later. Then, on February 6, 1788, Massachusetts approved with a vote of 187 to 168. Knox was delighted. All day long the bells rang out in Boston and other large cities while parades and celebrations filled the streets. The remaining states followed quickly in line, and the United States of America was born a strong and united nation.

The only thing that was needed now was a leader and, as might be expected, all eyes turned to one man. George Washington was unanimously chosen to be the first president of the United States.

And so, once again, the tall, quiet Virginian left his peaceful home at Mount Vernon and answered the call to lead his country. It was not his wish, but if the people willed it he would do his utmost to serve to the best of his ability. He wrote to Henry Knox: "I feel like a culprit going to his place of execution so unwilling am I, in the evening of a life nearly consumed in public cares, to quit a peaceful abode for an ocean of difficulties, without the competency of political skills, abilities and inclination which are necessary to manage the helm."

Henry Knox sent his congratulations, together with words of advice and encouragement. At Washington's request he also purchased five yards of fine, dark-brown homespun with which to make the new President's inaugural suit.

13

ON APRIL 23, 1789, a long line of gaily decorated barges and sailing craft made its way slowly across Newark Bay and into New York Harbor. It was led by a colorful row-galley bearing General George Washington on his way to the first presidential inauguration. Immediately behind it came an equally resplendent barge carrying Henry Knox, together with John Jay, the Secretary of Foreign Affairs and members of the Board of Treasury. Cannons boomed, flags and pennants waved jauntily in the breeze and a chorus of voices was raised in joyful song as the glittering flotilla moved into the wharf at the foot of Battery Park. Washington and the other dignitaries disembarked and marched up Broadway past throngs of surging people, all pushing and shoving to catch a glimpse of the first president of the United States.

A few days later, surrounded by eminent citizens and public officials, Washington stood on the balcony of Federal Hall, overlooking Broad and Wall Streets, and took the oath of office. Standing in a place of honor, only a few feet from the President, Henry Knox looked on. His heart swelled with pride at this singular distinction now being conferred on his old Commander-in-Chief.

When the ceremonies were over, there were celebrations and banquets throughout the city. That evening, the new president sat on the porch of Henry Knox's home and watched the brilliant display of fireworks, arranged in his honor.

When Washington selected his cabinet a few days later, he asked Henry Knox to stay on as his Secretary of War. Alexander Hamilton was appointed Secretary of the Treasury, Edmund Randolph became Attorney General and Thomas Jefferson Secretary of State. The astute and practical John Adams was Washington's Vice-President. It was a distinguished gathering of eminent and able men. Together these men, who had shared long years of suffering and defeat, would now share the trials and ordeals of the untested ship of state.

As Secretary of War under the new administration, Knox's first task was to brief the President on the tense and threatening Indian situation along the western border. Round-faced and plump, his left hand wrapped in the inevitable silk handkerchief, he paced the thick green carpet of Washington's anteroom. He was thirty-nine now, and his voice was deeper and more vibrant than ever.

"They're in a violent mood," he said. "The slightest provocation, the merest offense will give them excuse for attack. The Creeks and the Chickasaws in the south, the Mohawk and Iroquois in the north and the Shawnee and Cherokee along the Cumberland—all of them are bitter and resentful. If they can ever be united they will pose one of the gravest threats to our borders, to our very existence as a nation."

From the big chair behind his desk, Washington nodded. "And of course, the British and French would like nothing better."

"The Spanish too," said Knox.

Washington was staring out the window, deep in

thought. Five years ago he had personally traveled hundreds of miles along the border, on horse and on foot, to get a firsthand look at this new frontier. He was familiar with the country, and he knew the fighting qualities of its inhabitants. But he knew the settlers too, and he realized all too well that they would slowly, inevitably push the frontier ever further into the heartland of the west. His reply was almost a summary of his thoughts. "It will mean continuous strife for living space between the Indian and the white man."

"Precisely," said Knox. "But the point remains, do we have a clear right, under the principles of justice and law, to continue the destruction and expulsion of these savages? They were here first to possess the right of the soil, and it cannot be taken from them except by their consent or by right of conquest in a just war. As it is now, most of the troubles, raids and killings are the direct result of white incursion into treaty territories or retaliation for outrages perpetrated on the ignorant savage. North or south, the story is the same. As long as the settlers persist in moving into new territory, the consequences will be costly and bloody."

Washington was aware of all this, but with the continual increase of population there would be constant pressure on the government to open up new lands, regardless of laws, treaties or violence. What he was looking for was a way to pacify the savage and, at the same time, gain the lands necessary for growth and expansion. He was sure that America's destiny lay to the west.

"If we can obtain the rights to the land by treaty or consent," he said, "then so much the better. But if we are to have continued violence in this quarter, we have no other choice but to protect the settlers." He turned and looked directly at Knox. "What will this mean in the way of manpower and money?"

Henry Knox was an idealist. His politics were frequently mixed up with his humanitarianism. He believed in the rights of the Indians and looked upon them as fellow human beings. He wanted to assimilate them into the white man's society, to teach them to farm, to manufacture—most of all to accept them as citizens and brothers. But he knew this would take time. The Indian would resist with every fiber of his being. The white man would abhor the very thought. It would take generations, if not centuries. He had to face reality. He was a trusted agent of his government, and he had to think of that first. "To keep the Creeks and the other Indian nations of the south under control will require a force of at least two thousand, five hundred men at a cost of perhaps two hundred thousand dollars."

The President winced at the incredible figure as Knox continued.

"In the north the Iroquois and Mohawks can be held back with nothing less than two thousand, eight hundred men and an additional expenditure of another two hundred and thirty thousand dollars."

Washington got to his feet, shaking his head. "It's far too much. Congress will never stand for it. We couldn't possibly raise that kind of money in time of peace."

"Then the only answer is to continue to negotiate, to win the savages over by treaty and compromise and, at the same time, attempt to keep the settlers in line."

"Do you think that can be done?"

Once again Knox was forced to be realistic. "Yes, perhaps for a while, but it's entirely up to the whites. If the treaties are honored there will be peace. If not, there will be war."

Now it was Washington's turn to pace the floor. The final decision was up to him. As he had proved during the Revolution, he was a good field commander. He knew when to attack and when to retreat and now, above all, he needed time.

"All right then," he said. "We'll negotiate."

He took the matter before Congress a few days later and explained General Knox's position on the Indian situation. Knox was there to answer questions and provide additional information. Some of the members violently opposed the idea of bargaining with the savages, but when they heard the alternate cost of waging war they grudgingly consented to negotiations.

The acknowledged leader of the Indian nations in the south was a brilliant, well-educated halfbreed named Alexander McGillivray. His mother was the offspring of a full-blooded Creek maiden and a French cavalry officer. His father was a well-to-do Scotsman engaged in the Indian trade.

At fourteen, Alexander was sent to Charleston, where he received a white man's education, with tutoring in English, French and Latin. He later served as an apprentice in a Savannah counting house, where he acquired a wide knowledge of business and finance. His schooling finished, he returned to the family plantation at Little Tallasie in Georgia. There he helped supervise the huge estate, with its gardens and orchards, the long rows of cultivated fields, the many slaves and the herds of cattle and horses. With all this wealth, the McGillivrays had little to gain through revolution. When the war came, in 1776, they cast their lot with the Tories. As a result, a few years later, their holdings and stock were confiscated by the rebels and they were driven from the land.

Young Alexander was bitter and resentful. When his father gave up and returned to Scotland, Alexander chose to return to his mother's people and lead them in battle against the Americans. His education and intelligence soon made him a leader among the tribes.

Quick to realize his value as an ally, the British commissioned him a colonel, supplying him with guns and ammunition. With these and a strong force of Indian braves, he planned and led daring raids deep into Georgia and South Carolina, disrupting the rebels' supply lines and delaying their activities.

By the war's end he was the recognized titular and spiritual leader of the Creeks, the Chickasaws, the Cherokees and a large part of the Seminole nation; and he was rapidly inciting other tribes along the frontier to join his cause and push the settlers back across the Alleghenies. Now, with British and French support in the north and Spanish backing in the south, he was in a good position to accomplish exactly that.

Henry Knox knew that if the negotiations were going to result in any semblance of peace, McGillivray was the man they would have to talk to. With this in mind, he prevailed upon Congress to appoint a commission to meet with the Indian leader and determine his demands for a settlement. At first McGillivray stood aloof, refusing to deal with the Americans. But soon he heard rumors of gifts, large sums of money and an invitation to visit New York and he began to view the situation in a more favorable light, realizing that he might gain more by parley than by war.

With a colorful delegation of thirty Indian chiefs,

McGillivray arrived at Murray's Wharf, in New York, in the summer of 1790. Six feet tall, trim and stately, with dark, piercing eyes, McGillivray was an impressive sight as he stepped off the ferry, followed by his royal entourage of interpreters, servants and bodyguards. A full military escort, complete with regimental banners and brass bands, accompanied the party up Broadway to Federal Hall, where they were given a welcoming speech by the President and another by General Knox.

Their visit was filled with festivity and sightseeing. Artillary salutes were fired, bells tolled out the gala event and huge crowds of people came from miles around to stare at the strange-looking visitors.

A number of banquets were held in McGillivray's honor and, with great fanfare, he was elected an honorary member of the Tammany Society. The minor chiefs and other delegates were quartered in the Indian Queen Hotel, but McGillivray himself was the privileged guest of General and Mrs. Knox, who found him a fascinating and dynamic person.

McGillivray was pleased with his New York reception, but he did not let the flattery and adulation dull the edge of his bargaining powers. By a series of shrewd compromises he finally induced the government to agree to a treaty which left the Creek nation in virtually complete control of all the land they already held, and established a tentative boundary over which he was promised full protection from further encroachment. As an additional incentive he was appointed the official representative of the United States government to the Creek nation, with a rank of brigadier general and a salary of fifteen hundred dollars a year.

The treaty was signed on August 7 by the Secretary of

War, then by the thirty Creek delegates and finally by the President. To celebrate the occasion, the Indians donned full ceremonial regalia and performed a blood-curdling war dance around a roaring bonfire while thousands of spectators looked on. It was one of the first diplomatic transactions of the new administration, and it gave the infant nation a sense of gravity and importance.

But though the Indians in the south were temporarily appeased, the great nations of the Shawnee and the Iroquois in the north were still quarrelsome. They had stubbornly refused to attend such powwows and instead continued to resist any and all encroachments on their territory. Bloodthirsty raids, massacres and pillage were a daily occurrence. A number of punitive expeditions were sent out by the government to pacify the savages and protect the lives and property of the settlers, but these were undermanned and weak and frequently met with humiliating defeat or annihilation.

Yet, in spite of the treaties, in spite of the violence and defeats, the undaunted settlers slowly infiltrated into every part of the new frontier. And the Indians, failing to unite in common cause, were gradually, irrevocably exterminated or pushed back ever further towards the west.

Although Martha Washington, as the First Lady, was the official queen of government society, she had little interest in the planning and management of banquets, balls and levees. But sociable, bustling Lucy Knox was only too happy to take over these responsibilities. Together with Henry, she organized and conducted many of the state functions, attending to the proper arrangements of protocol, officiating at ceremonies and heading the re-

ception line at banquets and balls. Dressed in their eight-
eenth-century finery, Lucy and Henry were easily the
largest couple in the room, and they were never so happy
as when surrounded by large numbers of friends, political
officials, statesmen and visiting dignitaries. Theirs was
the world of hospitality and society, of the harpsichord
and the minuet. As for Washington, he agreed completely
with his first lady and was glad to leave the tedious duties
of entertaining in the competent hands of Lucy and Henry
Knox.

Henry had always been extravagant, but now, with the
unlimited opportunities for spending and entertaining, his
expenses far exceeded his income and he frequently found
himself deeply in debt. Fortunately he had acquired large
tracts of land in Maine, partly through Lucy's inheritance
and partly by purchase, and from time to time he found
it necessary to sell parcels of this acreage in order to
meet his growing financial obligations.

As might be expected, he was often reckless in his
commercial ventures and not always wise in his choice
of investments. It was not until later that he began to
learn the value of caution and moderation in business as
well as in life.

In 1790 the nation's capital was moved to Philadelphia,
there to await more permanent quarters, which were being constructed on the banks of the beautiful Potomac
River in Maryland. In the meantime the government met
and carried on its activities in the "City of Brotherly
Love."

Henry Knox and his family moved into a three-story
home on the north side of Chestnut Street, not far from
Independence Hall. Since Congress was not scheduled to
meet until December, there was a long interval of inac-

tivity through summer and fall. But even during such periods of waiting, Henry Knox was not idle. His agile mind was forever busy thinking up new projects. It was said that he often planned more in one day than he could possibly accomplish in a year. Among his proposals was a plan for a national militia that could be placed under the jurisdiction of the regular army in times of emergency, a forerunner of our present-day national guard. He advocated the establishment of a military academy at West Point and proposed a similar institution for the navy. He was continually fighting for an enlarged standing army, one adequate enough to protect the nation's boundaries and serve as a nucleus in case of war. He designed and erected a number of historical monuments commemorating landmarks and battles of the Revolution. He drew up plans for a canal between the Charles and Connecticut rivers in Massachusetts, which would greatly enhance the commercial possibilities of the region around Boston. He was a bear for work, indefatigable in his planning, always thinking ahead to the day when his country would be the strong, prosperous nation he had always dreamed of.

In 1793 Washington was re-elected to the presidency for a second term. It was during this period that France was going through the throes of her bloody revolution. At the same time, she was at war with England and, since she had recently befriended the patriots in their hour of need, it was only natural that she should look to America for help in her present struggle against a common enemy. But the United States was still weak. The government was inexperienced, the army was largely nonexistent. To provoke another war with England at this time would have been foolhardy and rash. For this reason Washington was determined to remain neutral.

The French sent over a special envoy by the name of Citizen Genet to plead for American support. But Genet turned out to be more than a soliciting emissary. He was, in fact, an unprincipled, audacious cad, a schemer of the worst sort. Within five days after landing on American soil he had opened up a number of recruiting stations to entice American youth into the French navy. He openly began commissioning American vessels as privateers, offering supplies and ammunition, literally setting up the mainland of the United States as a base from which to operate against England. Before long, French warships were bringing in captured English merchantmen, brazenly unloading them in American ports.

All these belligerent and aggressive acts did little to convince the British of America's neutral intentions. Again and again Genet was warned, both by the President and by the Secretary of State, to cease these warlike activities, but he continued to ignore the order and went right on with his illegal commissions.

Finally, in the summer of 1793, Genet incited an incident that threatened to bring England and the United States to the point of war. A British merchantman, the *Little Sarah,* had been captured by the French and brought into Philadelphia. There she lay, at anchor in the middle of the Delaware River, waiting for the Secretary of State to make arrangements with the British for her release.

The President was away at Mount Vernon and the Attorney General was off on a short vacation, but Jefferson hurriedly called a meeting of the remaining members of the cabinet. Henry Knox arrived at the Federal Building

to find Jefferson and Hamilton in heated conversation.
The Secretary of State was plainly disturbed. "We've just
received word that Genet is arming the *Little Sarah*," he
said. "He plans to send her out to sea as a French privateer."

Knox was stunned. "Impossible," he said. "The dis-
position of that ship is in American hands. The British
will be furious."

Hamilton was pacing the room. "The man is a fiend.
He'll drag us into this thing yet. We've got to do something before it's too late."

The Secretary of State held up a restraining hand.
"Gentlemen, let us be calm. Genet may still be prevailed
upon to listen to reason. The President will be back in a
few days. There is still time."

"Not if Genet decides to sail," said Knox. "I recom-
mend that we set up a battery of heavy guns on Mud
Island. Then we can blast her out of the water if she
attempts to leave."

"And have the entire French fleet down on our backs
within a few days," said Jefferson.

"It's either that or war with England," Knox warned.

"I agree with Henry," said Hamilton. "If that ship sails
it will create an international situation, one that we can
ill afford at this time."

Once again Jefferson called for caution. "Let me speak
with Genet. Perhaps I can persuade him to wait, at least
until the President gets here."

Henry Knox was shaking his head, still insisting that a
battery of artillery was the best solution. "It will act as
a strong deterrent, the one thing I'm sure Genet will
understand."

Hamilton nodded in agreement, but the matter was

held off until the President arrived on July 10, when, once again, they met behind closed doors. Jefferson briefed the President on the situation, stating that he had pleaded with Genet to hold off, but without success.

Washington was infuriated by the insolent attitude of the French minister.

"I still think we should set up artillery," said Knox.

Jefferson looked at the President. "Then we'll be taking the obvious risk of antagonizing the French."

Washington spoke slowly, trying to control his temper. "The question is a legal one," he said, "and must be resolved as such. The Supreme Court must hand down a decision on the status of the *Little Sarah*. Only then can we act."

The cabinet unanimously agreed, and a few days later the matter was turned over to the Supreme Court. But before the court could act, the *Little Sarah* slipped her moorings and sailed out to sea. Her career as a privateer had begun.

The government was stunned, and the nation held its breath as the ominous specter of another war loomed on the horizon. Henry Knox had been right. A half dozen guns, strategically placed, could have settled the issue before it began. Now it was too late.

Fortunately the British took a lenient view of the situation and did not exaggerate its warlike implications. Washington demanded the immediate recall of Citizen Genet, and a few weeks later the French government complied. Genet, fearful for his life, pleaded for sanctuary in the United States. Magnanimous as always, Washington granted the request and Genet retired quietly from the scene. He later married the daughter of Governor

Clinton of New York and settled down to the life of a gentleman farmer in the back reaches of the Hudson River valley.

14

AFTER THE REVOLUTION, the small beginnings of an American navy that had been established during the war were allowed to dwindle and decline. Congress and the new nation felt they had little to fear on the high seas. They were soon to learn differently. Piracy became a constant danger, and the Mediterranean ports in particular were hornets' nests of thieves and buccaneers. Besides this, both French and English privateers roamed the coast, capturing American vessels and impressing their crews.

Knox had long been an advocate of a strong navy, but his opinions and suggestions were consistently ignored. Now, as the raids and highjacking of ships became more serious, Congress finally approved the construction of six men-of-war. Under Knox's supervision, the keels were laid for the *United States,* the *Chesapeake,* the *Constitution,* the *Constellation,* the *President* and the *Congress.* Although none of these major battleships was completed during Knox's term of office, they were all, later, to play an important role in the glorious sea victories in the War of 1812.

The hot summer of 1793 brought the dreaded scourge of yellow fever to Philadelphia. It started down by the docks on Water Street and then spread rapidly until it reached every street and alley of the city. There was a mass exodus as hundreds and thousands of frightened people fled the stricken metropolis. The government offices were deserted. Washington was away at Mount Vernon and both Jefferson and Randolph were gone. The only members of the cabinet who still remained in the city were Henry Knox and Alexander Hamilton, and Hamilton was already down, deathly sick with the fever.

Knox personally picked up the reins of government. He ordered all clerks to a place of safety, then singlehandedly carried on the business of the administration. While people continued to die all around him and the death carts rattled through the streets, he did the work of the president, the secretary of state and the entire cabinet. Each week he sent Washington a full report on the state of the nation and also a brief account on the progress of the epidemic.

"The streets are lonely," he wrote, "almost deserted. Hundreds are dying and all the merchants have fled. Ships lay in the harbor unattended, banks are empty. It is almost as if an unseen enemy has occupied the city."

In the midst of all his labors, if Henry Knox had the time to look out the tall windows of the government building, he must surely have seen old Doctor Benjamin Rush, the well-known Revolutionary War surgeon, making his daily rounds, going from door to door, doing what he could to relieve the suffering. As a palliative, the doctor advised cleanliness and a light diet. During these long days and nights the good doctor slept little, and then only with his clothes on.

It wasn't long before Rush contracted the disease himself. Weak and exhausted, hardly able to stand, he continued to drag himself about the city, treating his patients. It was a determined, heroic effort, but all around him the unfortunate victims continued to wither and die.

Like Henry Knox, the Negro population of the city was strangely immune to the pestilence. Yet they refused to leave the stricken city. In spite of uncertainty and fear, they stayed on, to lend a helping hand, to care for the sick and bury the dead.

As the plague dragged on, week after interminable week, Washington finally ordered Knox to leave, and the Secretary of War made his way to Elizabethtown, New Jersey, and waited for the epidemic to subside.

From time to time Henry Knox had expressed a desire to resign from public affairs and retire to the comparative peace and quiet of private life, but each time he did the President had prevailed upon him to stay a few months longer. Now, as the last days of 1794 drew to a close, he again tendered his resignation. This time the words of the Secretary were so urgent, so convincing that the President could hardly find it in his heart to refuse.

"After having served my country for nearly twenty years," Knox pleaded, "the greatest portion of which was under your auspices, it is with extreme reluctance that I find myself constrained to withdraw from so honorable a situation. But the indispensable claims of a wife and a growing family of children, whose sole hopes of comfort rest upon my life and exertions, will no longer permit me to neglect duties so sacred.

"But in whatever situation I shall be, I shall recollect your confidence and kindness with all the fervor and purity of affection of which a grateful heart can be susceptible."

With a heart full of sadness, Washington replied, thanking Knox for his long and faithful service. "My personal knowledge of your exertions justifies the sincere friendship which I have ever borne for you and which will accompany you in every situation of life."

Henry Knox drew his salary for the final quarter of 1794, seven hundred and fifty dollars, and turned his steps towards the Province of Maine.

Many newspapers and journals throughout the country wished him Godspeed, while the *Official Gazette* of the United States praised him for his achievements and accomplishments, saying, in part, "The important service he rendered to the cause of liberty by his activity, zeal and perseverance, which were so conspicuous on every occasion, leave a deep impression on the mind of every friend of America."

By present-day standards the Knox holdings in Maine were enormous, comprising hundreds of square miles of virgin timberland between the Kennebec and Penobscot rivers. This vast tract had been largely inherited by Lucy from a land patent ceded to her great-grandfather under the original Plymouth Company. Henry later increased the property by additional purchase and grants. It was beautifully rugged country with rushing streams, clear lakes and endless forests of pine, hemlock and maple. Surveyed and explored by a trained geologist, it was found to contain some thirty-one varieties of minerals, together with valuable outcroppings of limestone and shale. Over thirty-two species of trees and hundreds of other plants and shrubs filled the dense landscape.

Henry Knox had never been a wealthy man and in order to raise money for the construction of his new home, he was forced to borrow heavily and sell more of his land. But, as might be expected, his ideas and plans were all drawn on a grandiose scale. He built one of the finest mansions in all New England. It was situated at the mouth of the Saint George River, overlooking Penobscot Bay. Three stories high, fronted by a tall cupola and a long flight of steps, it was simple yet imposing in design. Stately elms and spreading old oaks were spaced about the rolling lawns. Outbuildings, stables, cookhouses and a blacksmith shop made up the remainder of the estate.

After a long trip by stagecoach and boat the Knox family finally reached the landing place at Montpelier, the name Henry had given to his spacious enclave. With a feeling of awe and expectation they gazed up at the big mansion. Lucy, their firstborn, was nineteen now, well-poised and ladylike. Henry, Jr., sixteen, was spoiled and selfish, the result of too much attention. Next came Julia, thirteen, and William, almost ten. Little Agusta, eight, stood hand in hand with Caroline, almost four. Like a pack of frisky puppies they raced across the lawn and up the steps of the big white house that was to be their home. With a heart full of pride, Henry listened to their happy shouts of glee as they ran through the enormous rooms and flung open the shutters, to stare out the windows at the glittering landscape of water and pines. He stopped momentarily on the high portico to gaze down the ten miles of winding river. After twenty years of wandering, twenty years of work and sacrifice, he had finally come home.

To dedicate the new house and celebrate Independence Day, all in one, Henry decided to hold a gala banquet on the morning of July fourth. With the first light of dawn, the guests began to arrive. They came from all walks of life and from every segment of society—farmers and shopkeepers, bankers and the well-to-do, together with their families. They filed through the front door to stand amazed at the elegant oval lobby that towered fully four stories high, with bright sunshine streaming through the skylight overhead and glinting radiantly off the crystal chandelier hanging in the center. They passed through the hallway into the huge dining room, with its long sideboard, its stately rows of Chippendale chairs placed around the well-polished mahogany table, set with large pewterware platters, filled with steaming slices of lamb and beef, baked fish, roast chicken and duck, corn muffins, pies, plum puddings, fruits and desserts.

With all this elegance and grace, one wonders if perhaps Mrs. Knox did not stop for a moment and smile at the memory of the ill-advised prediction her father had made so many years ago, when he said, "You will dine on black bread and fish chowder while your sisters will live in the lap of luxury."

From the dining room the visitors made their way upstairs to the lavishly decorated bedrooms, where dozens of babies were tucked safely away while their mothers gadded about, admiring the draperies, the linens and the richly woven carpets. Most of them had never seen such splendor before.

Down in the music room, young Miss Lucy, charming and accomplished, played the harpsichord, surrounded by the young men and ladies of the neighborhood. All day long the guests continued to arrive, fascinated and amazed by the magnificent nineteen-room mansion, strolling about the gardens and across the shady lawns.

It was a happy occasion for Henry Knox, the proud master of Montpelier, as he mingled with the guests, discussing politics with the men, chatting with the ladies and patting the children on the heads. Later that evening, when all had departed, he stood on the portico, looking over his domain, happy and contented.

Henry Knox's hope for Maine was to see it grow into a prosperous and independent state. In this he was a pioneer, both in spirit and style of living. Lucy's piano was the first instrument of its kind ever brought into the region, while Henry's library was one of the largest in all of New England.

With his property established, Knox now proceeded to develop its resources. He set up a string of sawmills along the river to process timber floated down from the interior. He established brick kilns in and around the numerous clay deposits and quarried limestone and marble. He erected wharfs and docks and began a program of commercial fishing. And he established a shipyard for the construction of small vessels to take his lumber and farm produce to southern markets.

The farms and gardens around the estate were well kept and productive. Oxen, sheep and cattle grazed on the surrounding hillsides, while flocks of geese, chickens and ducks wandered about the premises. The stables housed as many as twenty horses, both for work and for riding. On Brigader Island, adjacent to his property, Knox set up an experimental breeding station, importing cattle, sheep and hogs and crossing the hardy native stock with foreign varieties to improve the breed.

To operate all these ventures he hired quarrymen, brickmakers, carpenters, shipwrights, coopers, blacksmiths, artisans, gardeners and millwrights, employing as many as a hundred workmen at a time.

With all this enterprise and industry going on, the nearby village of Thomaston soon became a busy, thriving community. Stores and roominghouses sprang up along its winding streets, and its population nearly doubled. To add to the spiritual life of the settlement, Knox contributed toward the construction of a church. He also donated the windows and a large brass bell, cast and finished by the noted silversmith Paul Revere.

To develop his outlying holdings, Knox advertised for settlers. They were given clear titles to the property they purchased and in turn were expected to till the land and raise such foodstuffs and commodities as the surrounding community required. As usual, Henry Knox was living and planning beyond his means, and he was frequently forced to go into debt to keep the sheriff from his door. On one occasion, he borrowed ten thousand pounds sterling, about $48,000, putting up three thousand acres of choice land as security.

Throughout his life, no matter where he lived, no matter what his circumstances, Henry Knox was always openhearted and generous. His home and his pocketbook were ever open to the dispossessed, the political refugee and those in need. He cared for and helped to raise several of Lucy's nephews, who were sent over from England after the war. During the French Revolution, the son of the Marquis de Lafayette lived in the Knox household until it was safe to go back to France. Still another political refugee from France was the Duke de Liancourt, who found a ready welcome in the Knox home. At the time, the Duke said, "I have three dukedoms on my head and not a coat on my back." He never forgot Henry Knox, who gave him both a home and the coat he so badly needed.

The Knox household was always happy and cheerful. The children were given the run of the house, and Henry never tired of listening to their joyous laughter as they went about their work and play. But life at Montpelier was not all fun and pleasure. There were times of grief and sorrow too.

Henry's brother, William, who had been a part of the family, off and on, ever since the early days in Boston, was confined to a mental institution in Pennsylvania. Over the years his health had declined rapidly, and his mental outlook became increasingly morbid and depressed. Henry continued to provide for his care and welfare until 1795, when, after a lingering illness, William finally passed away.

At a time when little was known about the mysterious ills of man and even less about how to cure them, tragedy and death often lurked unexpectedly just around the corner. Of the twelve children whom Mrs. Knox had brought into the world, only six had survived. Five died in childbirth or infancy, and another, a boy, died at an early age as the result of an accident in boarding school.

Now again, in 1796, the big mansion at Montpelier was caught up in the cruel uncertainty of life and death as two of the children, Agusta, nine, and William, eleven, were stricken with the suffocating spasms of what was then called throat distemper, today known as diphtheria. For two days the big house was wrapped in gloom as Henry and Lucy Knox paced the floor while the doctors did what little they could to relieve the suffering. For two days there was no laughter or sound of voices. All work, all activity came to a standstill. The caretakers, the servants and gardeners watched the big mansion, praying silently, waiting for a sign of hope. Then, on the third day, the doors opened and the sad news was announced. The children had died. For months the bereaved parents tried to forget, tried to carry on, but even before their young ones were cold in the grave, another daughter, Julia, died of consumption. It was a tragic blow, but it happened in an era when such incidents were all too common.

Henry had other setbacks too. Fishing was not always profitable, his livestock often died of disease and high tides and winter ice frequently destroyed his wharfs and damaged his shipping. Whenever these financial losses occurred he was forced, once again, to sell more of his land or go deeper into debt. It was a constant struggle just to make ends meet.

The Knox holdings were spread out over hundreds of square miles of virgin timberland, too distant for close supervision. Over the years numerous squatters had moved in and settled on the land. At first Knox paid little attention to the intruders, but as their numbers increased, reaching into the hundreds, he became concerned. He wanted settlers, not squatters.

By 1801 the situation had reached a climax. Knox's surveyors and woodcutters were frequently harassed by squatters disguised as Indians. Ironically enough, when Henry threatened to take the matter to court the squatters rose up in armed rebellion. Since many of them were veterans of the Revolution, Knox had no wish to prosecute. Instead he called them together at his home to explain the legal aspects of the situation. Then he offered to sell them the land for sixty-six cents an acre, with long-term contracts to pay it off.

The squatters were amazed. They knew the land was worth at least ten dollars an acre, yet this man, who a moment ago had been their enemy, was willing to sell them the property for less than a tenth of its normal value. Smiling and bowing, their animosity completely gone, they went up to him, shook his hand and thanked him for his generosity. Over six hundred of them immediately signed the deeds, and the others followed a short while later.

On another occasion, however, Henry Knox's generosity was stretched beyond the limits of human endurance. A large clan of Indians, known as the Tarratine tribe, lived and made their hunting grounds in the wilderness areas adjacent to the Knox property. To create an atmosphere of friendship and goodwill, Henry invited them to an old-fashioned barbecue.

For days the Indians continued to arrive, coming in out of the wilderness with their squaws and papooses, setting up camp in and around the lawns and gardens about the house. A huge feast was prepared, complete with venison, beef, corn bread, sweetmeats and cider. Games and contests were held, along with periods of dancing and singing. The feasting and ceremonies were repeated the next day and the next. After weeks of celebration Henry Knox's supplies were running low; yet the Indians showed no sign of leaving. Finally, with considerable tact and understanding, Knox approached the chief.

"Your visit has been honorable," he said, "and I have enjoyed the company of my wilderness friends. But many moons have passed and it is time that the braves went back to their hunting and the squaws returned to their homes." The old chief smiled and held up his hand in agreement, but it was still many days before the Indians packed up their belongings and returned to the wilderness. By this time both Henry's larder and his hospitality were equally exhausted.

Yet, in spite of all this extravagant living, in spite of his generosity and wild speculation, Henry Knox's business ventures began to pay off. As the years passed, his shipbuilding prospered and his coastal vessels were carrying bricks, lumber and farm produce as far south as Norfolk, Virginia. His stock raising improved and his stables finally numbered twenty-two fine horses. For the first time, the estate began to show a profit. At long last his goal was fulfilled. He had become the gentleman farmer, the successful businessman that he had always dreamed of being.

During the long winter evenings Henry Knox loved to relax, with his family gathered around him, and watch Mrs. Knox play chess with one of the guests or listen to young Lucy pick out a melody on the harpsichord. It was during this time that he wrote to a friend. "I am more happy now than at any other period of my adult life."

15

THROUGHOUT HIS LONG YEARS of private life, Henry Knox never forgot the many friends he had made during those active days as artillery commander in the Revolution or as Secretary of War, nor did he lose touch with the important events that affected the government and the nation. He still wrote letters to Washington, briefing him on his plans and activities, almost as if he were still under the old General's command. He also continued a voluminous correspondence with such men as Thomas Jefferson, John Adams, Thomas Mifflin, the Marquis de Lafayette, Admiral de Grasse, Baron von Steuben and dozens of other men from all walks of life whose judgment and friendship he had come to respect and admire. He was a prodigious writer, and his letters number in the thousands.

When Washington left the presidency at the end of his second term, he wrote to Knox describing his feelings, ending with: "It is not without regrets that I am parting from the few intimates whom I love, among these be assured you are one."

Knox congratulated Washington on his long service to his country and wished him well as he once again entered private life. Then he wrote to the new president, his longtime friend John Adams. "I doubt whether I should congratulate you on being elevated to the Chief Magistry of the United States, for it is questionable whether there are not more thorns than roses in the situation."

Adams replied, "If I should meet with any roses in my path I shall thank you for the congratulations, and also when I set my foot on thorns, as I certainly shall, I shall thank you equally for your condolences."

In 1798, relations with France had reached a crisis. In spite of constant warnings and official protests, French privateers continued to harass American shipping, and war seemed imminent. Washington was hastily called back to lead the army and draw up a proposal for a new general staff. When Henry Knox read the list he was stunned. He had been placed third in command under General Alexander Hamilton, a man who had been one of his artillery captains during the late war. For the first time in his career Knox questioned Washington's judgment. Hurt and indignant, he refused to serve except in the case of an invasion.

Fortunately war did not materialize, although a number of encounters occurred between American and French warships on the high seas.

As the weeks passed, Knox soon forgot the misunderstanding. He was too big a man to hold a grudge, and he and Washington once again became the best of friends— but not for long, for a few months later the old General died at his home at Mount Vernon. Henry Knox was saddened, as was the rest of the nation, at the loss of his great friend and hero. Yet he was not depressed. "I perceive no cause for regret," he said, "at the departure of our old chief. He exhibited a most glorious setting sun."

In the early years of the eighteen hundreds Knox was in his fifties, still in the autumn of his life. He had grown prudent and experienced, wise in the ways of the world. He saw his farms and his business ventures producing a small but steady income. He saw his daughter, Lucy, grow up, marry and start a family of her own. He was elected to the Massachusetts legislature, and he once again became a familiar figure in the society and political life of Boston. As he mellowed with age and wisdom, he became less impulsive and more philosophical. In 1806 he wrote, "The years roll away and soon we shall be numbered among those who have been atoms upon this atom of a globe and very soon after, it will be forgotten that we had any existence here at all."

All his life Henry Knox had dearly loved to eat, and it took a considerable amount of food to nourish that portly frame. Now, in October, the big dinner table at Montpelier was filled with an ample harvest. There were simmering rich, golden-brown turkeys, tender duckling, baked fish, vegetables, cheese, cornbread, pumpkin pies, fruit and puddings, all cooked and prepared in the huge basement kitchen. It was at one of these sumptuous meals that Henry accidentally swallowed a splinter of chicken bone. A few hours later the jagged sliver of bone pierced the wall of his intestine, producing a severe abdominal infection. Feverish and weak, Henry lay in bed, fighting against the pain, while the doctors did their utmost to perform a cure. Optimistic as always, Knox was certain that he would soon be well. He even wrote to a friend, whose home he had been planning to visit. "I am detained by an indisposition which will probably prevent my setting out this week," implying, of course, that he would be able to travel soon. This time, unfortunately, his optimism was of no avail—for five days later he was dead.

All over the nation those who had known this hearty, jovial man mourned his passing. He had loved his country above all else, and had served it faithfully for almost half his life. He had fought tyranny and oppression with patriotism and courage, he had conquered pessimism and gloom with wit and humor. Quietly and without fanfare he had been a benefactor to many.

As befitted his status, his burial had all the pomp and ceremony of a full military funeral. A huge crowd gathered at Montpelier to see the great artilleryman make his last journey. The services were performed in the big mansion, after which the solemn procession moved along the corridors and out onto the spacious lawns. Here it was escorted by a troop of local militia, an artillery company and a detachment of cavalry. Muffled drums beat out a steady dirge as the black coffin was carried to its resting place. The General's favorite horse followed close behind, its master's boots reversed in the stirrups. The bell in the church steeple tolled out the sad message of farewell, and on a distant hilltop, a cannon thundered a last salute. Flags were lowered to half-mast as General Henry Knox was laid to rest beneath the spreading branches of a gnarled old oak.

No longer would the halls of Montpelier resound to the booming laughter of this big man who loved life so well. No longer would the chambers of government echo to the ring of his voice. The man who was a friend to all men, a compatriot of statesmen, an adviser to presidents, was no more. He lived during a time in history when his abilities and strength were a boon to a struggling nation.

Fighting side by side with his beloved Commander-in-Chief, he remained steadfast and unflinching, never doubting, never faltering in his loyalty and willingness to serve. When all about him were deserting and giving up, he found new courage and, against incredible odds, inspired others to carry on the fight. When the new nation was experiencing its first pangs of uncertainty and doubt, he again met the challenge and helped to steady the floundering ship of state. He never once gave way to fear, doubt or despondency. To Washington he was like a rock of strength in a raging whirlpool of conflict and uncertainty.

Since his death, the influence Henry Knox exerted on the formation of his country has often been overlooked. While others have frequently been eulogized in song and legend, his name has too often gone unsung. Douglas Southall Freeman, the noted biographer of Washington, once remarked that the most neglected hero of the Revolutionary War was General Henry Knox. In his book, *The Founding Fathers,* Nathan Schachner describes Knox's abilities and influence on his times as greatly underrated.

Yet he has not been entirely forgotten. In cities, counties and places across the country his name dots the landscape. From Nebraska to Maryland, from Canada to Georgia, there are ten Knoxvilles, nine Knox counties and at least six other cities that bear his name. The well-known home of the United States gold reserve at Fort Knox was named in his honor. The route of his famous artillery march from Fort Ticonderoga to Boston is marked by a series of bronze plaques. Medals and awards in his name, are given annually by The Sons of the Revolution. The Society of The Cincinnati, the philanthropic

organization that he established in 1784, is still in existence, still carrying on its good works, as Henry Knox
intended that it should.

For years the Knox family continued to live on at the
big mansion, Mrs. Knox going into seclusion, pining for
her Henry. She died in 1824 after a lingering illness, at
the age of sixty-eight. Henry Knox, Jr., finally settled
down to become a pious churchman and respectable citizen. He died in 1832 and, as a self-imposed punishment
for his reckless youth, asked to be buried in an unmarked
grave. The youngest daughter, Caroline, married John
Holmes, the first United States Senator from Maine. She
died in 1851. Lucy, the firstborn of the Knox children,
lived on until 1854. Her son, Henry Knox Thatcher, a
rear admiral in the U.S. Navy, inherited the estate, but
he was unable to keep it up. It was torn down in 1871,
and part of the servants' quarters were converted into the
Thomaston railway station.

For many years the old estate was forgotten and allowed to deteriorate and decay. Then, in 1927, interest
was revived and the value of the site as an historical shrine
was realized. The General Knox chapter of the Daughters
of the American Revolution began raising money to re-
build the old mansion. Cyrus Curtis of the Curtis Publishing Company donated $240,000, and in 1929 a new
building was constructed, an exact replica of the Montpelier of 1800. The grounds were replanted and land-
scaped with fine, spacious lawns and shade trees. Many
of the original furnishings were located, reconditioned
and brought back to grace the majestic rooms. Today the
splendor of Montpelier lives again, just as it was when
its portly master strode its halls and filled its corridors
with his booming laughter.

And outside, under the shadows of the old shade trees, stands the headstone of General Henry Knox with this simple inscription:

'Tis fate's decree, farewell thy just renown
The hero's honor and the good man's crown.

BIBLIOGRAPHY

American Heritage (eds.). *The American Heritage Book of The Revolution*. New York: American Heritage, 1958.

Bill, Alfred Hoyt. *Valley Forge: The Making of an Army*. New York: Harper & Brothers, 1952.

Billias, George A. (ed.). *George Washington's Generals*. New York: William Morrow & Co., 1964.

Billias, George A. *General John Glover and His Marblehead Mariners*. New York: Henry Holt & Co., 1960.

Blakeless, John. *Turncoats, Traitors and Heroes*. Philadelphia: J. B. Lippincott Co., 1959.

Bowen, Catherine D. *Miracle at Philadelphia: The Story of the Constitutional Convention. May-September, 1787*. Boston: Little, Brown & Co., 1966.

Brooks, Noah. *Henry Knox: A Soldier of the Revolution*. New York: G. P. Putnam's Sons, 1900.

Callahan, North. *General Washington's General: Henry Knox*. New York: Rinehart Co., Inc., 1958.

Chidsey, Donald B. *Victory at Yorktown*. New York: Crown Publishers, 1962.

Commager, Henry S., and Morris, Richard B. *The Spirit of 'Seventy-Six*. 2 Vols. Indianapolis: Bobbs-Merrill, 1958.

Downey, Fairfax. *Sound of the Guns: The Story of the American Artillery*. New York: David McKay Co., 1955.

Drake, F. S. *Life and Correspondence of Henry Knox*. Boston, 1873.

Dupuy, Ernest R., and Trevor N. *The Compact History of the Revolutionary War*. New York: Hawthorn Books Inc., 1963.

Fiske, John. *The American Revolution*. 2 Vols. Boston: Houghton Mifflin Co., 1901.

Fleming, Thomas J. *Beat the Last Drum: The Battle of Yorktown*. New York: St. Martin's Press, 1963.

Flexner, James T. *The Traitor and the Spy: Benedict Arnold and John André*. New York: Harcourt, Brace & Co., 1953.

Flicks, Alexander C. *General Henry Knox's Ticonderoga Expedition*.

New York State Historical Association Proceedings Vol. XXVI and Quarterly Journal, IX, 1928, pp. 119-135.

Freeman, Douglas S. *George Washington: A Biography*. 6 Vols. New York: Charles Scribner's Sons, 1948-1954.

French, Allen. *The Siege of Boston*. New York: Macmillan Co., 1911.

Jacobs, James R. *The Beginning of the U.S. Army*. Princeton, New Jersey: Princeton University Press, 1947.

Jensen, Merrill. *The New Nation: A History of the United States During the Confederation, 1781-1789*. New York: Alfred A. Knopf, Inc., 1950.

Krout, John A. *The Completion of Independence, 1779-1830*. New York: Macmillan Co., 1944.

Lancaster, Bruce. *From Lexington to Liberty*. New York: Doubleday Co., 1955.

Leiby, Adrian C. *The Revolutionary War in the Hackensack Valley*. New Brunswick, New Jersey: Rutgers University Press, 1962.

Lossing, Benson J. *Pictorial Field Book of the American Revolution*. 2 Vols. New York: Harper & Brothers, 1851.

Montross, Lynn. *Rag, Tag and Bobtail: The Story of the Continental Army, 1775-1783*. New York: Harper & Brothers, 1952.

Neuman, George C. *History of the Weapons of the American Revolution*. New York: Harper & Row Publishers, 1967.

Rossiter, Clinton. *The Grand Convention, 1787*. New York: Macmillan Co., 1966.

Schachner, Nathan. *The Founding Fathers*. New York: G. P. Putnam's Sons, 1961.

Scheer, George F., and Rankin, Hugh B. *Rebels and Redcoats*. New York: World Publishing Co., 1957.

Sergent, Winthrop. *The Life and Career of Major John André*. New York: William Abbatt, 1902.

Stryker, William S. *The Battles of Trenton and Princeton*. Boston: Houghton Mifflin Co., 1898.

Thacher, James. *Military Journal of the American Revolution*. Hartford, Connecticut: Silas Andrus & Son, 1862.

Trevelyan, George O. *The American Revolution*. 6 Vols. London: Longmans, Green & Co., 1909-1914.

Van Every, Dale. *Ark of Empire: The American Frontier, 1784-1803*. New York: William Morrow & Co., 1963.

Ward, Christopher. *The War of the Revolution*. 2 Vols. New York: Macmillan Co., 1952.

INDEX

ABOUT THE AUTHOR

DURING WORLD WAR II, Justin Denzel served in Europe. Before that time, he worked as a field naturalist for the American Museum of Natural History. He sailed aboard the research vessel *Atlantis* on an oceanographic expedition, and spent two years in Alaska collecting marine life and working as a wildlife reporter for the local press. Always an avid reader, he enjoys everything from history and philosophy to science, exploration and literature. He has been writing most of his life, specializing in history and adventure stories for young people for the past ten years, and has published over a hundred stories and articles and two books. He now lives in Clifton, New Jersey, with his wife and son, and works in the Scientific Library of Hoffmann-La Roche, a large pharmaceutical firm in Nutley, New Jersey.